The Drive
Up From Tucson

Susan O'Byrne

The Drive Up From Tucson

TABLE OF CONTENTS

for Owen and Nora

SNOWBIRD SEASON

She's back again. That tiny, bent woman is back strolling the Farmers Market again this morning. She's been here the past three Saturdays. She looks to be in her seventies, short and humped. As if in defiance of her age and posture, she wears full make-up, eyeshadow and lipstick. Her hair, steel-wool grey, is tightly curled as if fresh from the salon. She wears a banana yellow tee shirt and white capri pants, with red flip-flop sandals. I notice a red bangle bracelet matching the sandals, a nice touch. It is 7:30 in the morning. She is flawlessly put together, but God help me, the woman is hideous. Really. She looks like a troll who lives under a bridge.

Well, I sort of figure I'm going to hell, so why stop now? Honestly, though, she is breath-takingly homely, which may explain all the make-up. It doesn't help that everyone around here looks so darned *comfortable*. As usual. I'm glad I'm hidden here behind my table, all my products serving as protective coloring. Nobody ever notices the vendors here. They come to see one another.

I sip my iced tea as she strolls by all the booths, glancing at the locally-sourced honeys, the kombuchas and vegan crepes (for the healthy hipsters), before stopping at Tamara's bread place. Rising Crumb. I love that place too. Over-priced as hell but oh, my goodness, it's so chewy and delicious. Just the right amount of crunch. Tamara always has samples and they are amazing. Even when they're all dried out at the end of the day, I love them.

This time, the little old lady brought (I imagine) her daughter and granddaughter with her. The daughter is lovely (go figure), probably thirty-ish, and wearing a wildly patterned paisley maxi-dress. Her hair is long and beach-curly. The grand-daughter is maybe three or four. She wears a backpack shaped like a colorful elephant, a batik-like print. She hugs her troll grandma's white leg

2

and I realize how much of a narrow-minded jerk I'm being. Clearly, there is someone for everyone. Even Grandma Troll has a loving family. I'll bet the little girl likes to play with all the billy-goats they've collected.

"Oh, look, sweetie!" says paisley-dressed lady. "Cookies!" They've now turned towards my booth. All my mean-spirited jokes at their expense fall away. Now they are the perfect little buying trio.

"The Flour Shop," Grandma reads. "The *Flour* Shop! Oh, I get it."

"Can I have a cookie, Mommy?" asks the little girl with the elephant backpack. "Please?"

They look over today's selections. Sugar cookies decorated with royal icing. We have flowers (pink, blue, purple and red), little saguaros, baseball gloves (it is February in Arizona after all), and Valentine hearts. Tis the season. I really wish I could display my cakes, though. I have some amazing cakes over at the free-standing store I've got on Pueblo Street in Tempe. But cakes don't hold up well in the outdoor market; buttermilk frosting in the heat is a disaster.

I give the trio a sample – really, just a damaged cookie I couldn't sell. Grandma seems particularly impressed. Once again, I should be ashamed of myself for my unkind thoughts earlier. Oh, well.

"Is that a little citrus in them?" she asks.

"It's orange zest," I reply. "You have a good palate."

"That's just how my mother used to make them," Granny says.

I nod, smiling, and say, "Mine, too!"

Granny and company buy a half dozen cookies, flowers and hearts.

I lied. My mom never made decent cookies beyond your garden variety Toll House. She stopped cooking entirely a few years before she died, which was a really good thing. Honestly. Mom had completely lost her sense of taste long before Covid popularized it. It was really weird. Seemingly overnight, her food, which, admittedly, had never been award-winning, lost any trace of flavor. It was like eating Styrofoam. This wasn't entirely Mom's fault, though; when she first got sick, her doctors told her she couldn't have anything even remotely spicy or salty, so she had to change up the way she prepared everything. And then I think she just got used to it.

I work the Old Town Scottsdale Farmers Market whenever I can, especially during Spring Training. February is bananas here in the Valley. I make more money in a few weekends of winter Famers Markets than I do in June through September combined. You've got to get up early to set up your stand, of course, but I'm a baker; I'm always up early. The market runs 7:00 am to 1:00 pm in the winter. Perfect. The market begins with the early-riser coffee crowd and finishes off with the lunch gangs. Lucky for me, both groups eat cookies.

Kelly Vargas with Desert Mirage Alpaca Ranch has the booth to my left. Her table is covered with sweet little fuzzy socks and purses; those are her biggest sellers. You can never have too many warm alpaca wool socks in the middle of Phoenix, right? Though, really, you'd be surprised how chilly a December night in the Valley can be. Not to mention up in Flagstaff or Williams, where you can go skiing just two hours away. I always like it when I'm placed near Kelly because the people who like

5

cutesy socks tend to like cookies. She has some darling ones, striped like candy canes. They're silly and frivolous, but people buy them. The same goes for Carefree Honey, with their precious little jars.

I never do as well when they put me near Fit Mama Foods (something about putting full-fat sugar cookies next to vegan almond strawberry protein energy bars just seems weird) or one of the endless booths that sell lotions, moisturizers, tinctures, oils, aroma therapies. My biggest gripe is when they put me near Helena, better known as The Beignet Babe. Our products are just a little too similar, though she makes each little fried donut to order. Her fryers always end up broiling me as well. Same goes for Matthew, the taco guy. Folks do like to get a sweet bite after the tacos, but you don't want to be right alongside them. The people just don't want to get their dessert right next to lunch. It's weird, I know. I don't make the rules.

The people-watching at this Farmers Market is pure gold. From the red-cheeked, paunchy fellows in their pastel golf shorts to the brittle, antique mahogany gals wearing floppy hats, bright red lipstick and bangles on their matchstick arms to the sunburned, tattooed goofball young men in fraternity shirts to the endless influx of loud young women who travel in giggly packs. I honestly love these groups of women. They refuse to admit they would actually *eat a meal*, but think nothing of dropping $4.95 on a fancy cookie decorated to look like a cactus, plus a few to bring home. They even buy my Flour Shop logo stickers, which even I will admit are a rip-off for a dollar. They take pictures of themselves holding my cookies or biting into my cookies as they uniformly huddle, crouched, near my booth. Each holding an iced coffee in their non-cookie hand. Sometimes it's a group of bridesmaids, or a baby shower, or a 30th/40th/50th birthday.

I've even had a couple Divorce Party packs of females. Really, they fly into Sky Harbor from St. Louis or Denver or Seattle just so they can cheer up their divorcing friend. It's amazing. I'm just so baffled that they all want to celebrate their divorces. If Pat and I ever got divorced, all I'd want to do is lie in bed watching *Grey's Anatomy* and eating Hot Pockets. So, yay for them. Plus, the divorcees are great tippers. Above and beyond the price of an order.

These gals are a new breed for the 21st Century. They have one goal: spend money, but in an Instagram-able way. Take as many phone photos as possible and post them on social media for their friends at home. It's a win-win, as far as I'm concerned. I cheer them all on. You would not believe the kind of special orders I've gotten for these ladies' parties. You know, the sexy stuff for the bridal showers and the boob jobs (yes, they have parties for that out here; welcome to Scottsdale, plastic surgery capitol of the Southwest!) Even a tough old broad like me blushes at the shapes they want some of their cookies and cakes in. Body parts. You get the idea. I happily honor their requests; I have a special set of cookie cutters for those occasions. Mom would have cackled at that, and then pretended to be scandalized. But Mom's no longer with us.

When she was around, of course, Mom liked to remind me that I have a supremely fucked up relationship with food. "Quit eating your feelings," she'd snap at me. Or: "You've been stress-eating again, I can always tell." Mom's powers of observation made me nervous, the same way skinny people have been making curvy people feel nervous for time immemorial. I'm sure she didn't *mean to be* a jerk about it; I'm sure she probably *believed* that she was helping me, even. Either way, it messed me up for years. Still does sometimes. And wouldn't Mom be proud of herself for that one? That she can still control my actions years after she shuffled off this mortal coil? The punchline here is that, despite, or maybe because of, my mother's constant kvetching about my eating habits, I now bake for a living.

Naturally. Why spend loads of money on a therapist when I can self-diagnose? An unhealthy relationship to food, you say? Worried about eating, you say? Well then, why not decide to spend ten hours a day surrounded by sugar and buttercream and eggs and chocolate as a result? Hmmm. Oh, and Doctor Freud, it gets even wackier than that: my career also began as the result of a bad break-up. I really missed my calling as an amateur shrink, at least when it comes to self-diagnosis. I may be a hot mess most days of the week, but I do pride myself on being self-aware.

Here we go. Back in the day, when I was young and carefree, I took some classes in Dental Hygiene over at Mesa Community College. I was being practical, not stupid like my brother, wasting stacks of money on Philosophy classes at ASU. Now *that* was money thrown away. I had a vision and I followed it. And once I got through that awful class on Anatomy of the Head and Neck, which was pretty gnarly, I did pretty well. Honestly, it was pretty fun. I learned how to do x-rays, administer fluoride, and put in sealants. All sorts of interesting stuff.

I was working a shift at the Dental Hygiene Clinic near the Baywood Medical Center one evening, when in walks Dental Student Jamie, DDS-to-be. Looking all shiny and confident and wavy-haired. Jamie was a laugher. The type of guy who knows he's charming and just can't help himself; he needs to laugh at everything he says. And he was terribly charming. At least, I thought so. Way more charming than the rest of the crowd you meet at Hygiene School, ninety percent of whom are female anyway. Ye Olde Sexism is still fully engrained in the dentistry biz. All the dentists are male, and their helpmates are all female.

Jamie and I dated his way through the College of Dental Medicine in Glendale. We were the Perfect Pair, in fact. I worked full-time at the Target on Power Road in Mesa, while taking classes at night and subsidizing Jamie's career. I have to give Jamie some credit: he was both charming and clever. He never said *out loud* that I should do his laundry and cook for him and run his little errands to CVS and Basha's. Instead, he'd look up at me with those great big puppy dog eyes and say how he worried he was that he was going to do poorly on his next exam on gum disease or something. And that maybe he shouldn't be hanging out with me so much and should concentrate more on his studies. And I'd get all worried that Jamie was jeopardizing his Big Dental Career to spend time with frivolous little me. Full-on Guilt would kick in, and I'd jump up and wash his underwear and pay for his Lucky Charms.

In retrospect, it's all blatantly obvious, but back then I was young and stupid and starry-eyed. A couple years later, Jamie got the all-important DDS behind his name, and suddenly we (meaning he) "needed to move on" from our relationship. As if we hadn't spent all those years prepping the way for the perfect little clean-toothed family.

I was blind-sided and went a little bonkers. Ok, a lot bonkers. I stalked Jamie, I drank myself silly, and I laid on the sofa all day. Mom very helpfully called me up one day and told me to snap out of it, get off my ass and grow up. Of course, I couldn't bear the idea of working in a dental office after that. I rebelled. And my rebellion went by way of sugar. I starting baking.

I started with chocolate chip cookies and went on to fancy shortbread. I experimented with recipes and developed a sugar cookie that kept its shape through baking, held frosting well, and didn't taste like dust. I taught myself how to decorate with fancy Royal Icing. My cupcakes were tender and never too crumbly: chocolate, vanilla bean, carrot cake and red velvet. I bought huge mixers and custom cookie cutters. I was constantly innovating.

In other words, I took out a shit ton of loans.

Every day in America, there are thousands of gals who bake tasty treats and think they can make a living at it. The next Mrs. Fields. They last about a year, if they are lucky. And after all their friends have referred her to all their friends, the demand dries up and the promising home baker packs up her oven mitts and slinks away. And sometimes there's a gal who gets lucky. Maybe she lives near a touristy area where the wealthy like to play? Maybe she discovered she is pretty good making an online presence for herself in the form of blogs, Facebook, and Instagram? Maybe her cupcakes, cakes and cookies *are Just That Good*?

At any rate, I was able to rent some industrial sized ovens and display cases and mixers, found a storefront on Pueblo Street in Tempe, bullied my way into having a *presence* in every one of the high-end farmers markets in the greater Phoenix area, and the Flour Shop was born. Yes, I am still massively in debt. But the business is still growing. I have shipped cookies to Baltimore and Coral Gables! I've appeared on *Good Morning, Arizona* for a two minute spot on local businesses. I was one of about a half dozen vendors, but word gets out. At any rate, I'm doing just fine and Jamie DDS can go fuck himself.

Most importantly, at least I had the good sense to meet Patrick in the messy wake of the Jamie years. We met online, which is the only decent place to meet someone these days, if you're over twenty-five and not into the bar-hopping scene like all of those the cougars in North Scottsdale. Patrick is literally the most wonderful man in the world, even if he can be clueless sometimes. Pat helped shepherd The Flour Shop into being. He kept me positive, he always, always encouraged me. God knows, he also invested his own time and cash.

None of this was overnight, mind you. It's taken me years to get the Flour Shop to be the moderate success that it is. There were plenty of times that I wanted to give up. But Pat wouldn't let me. Mom wouldn't either. And by that, I mean, I just couldn't bear the thought of hearing her tell me "I told you so" when my business failed. So I stuck it out and here we are.

And we had our baby, Austin, who is still my baby, though now much taller than me and going to school down at the University of Arizona. The idea of him becoming a productive member of modern society in a year or two is difficult to visualize. These days, Austin just wants to listen to music and drink with his friends. Was I any different at his age? Well, it was a different world back then. Patrick says I worry too much about Austin; the kid'll be just fine. But Patrick is a special kind of human who is just at peace with the universe in a way that I will never be.

Patrick's got a kiddie concert to bartend for tonight. In general, the kiddie concerts are not that great, but the bar will get decent action from the parent chaperones hanging around there during the performance, rather than jamming out on the floor. Patrick always lends an understanding and sympathetic ear to the guests, so he does pretty well on tips, if not in total sales on nights like these. The man has the patience of a saint, I swear. I don't know how he does it. But Pat gets a kick out of it.

Kiddie concerts aren't as hard on his ears as when they have a metal band playing at the Lounge. Patrick tells me the hardest part is getting used to the high-pitched caliber of the young girls' screams. Their moms and dads will hang out at the bar with Pat all night, drinking and maybe ordering an order of nachos or something, while the teenage heartthrob plays their little heart out onstage. The kiddos will probably too captivated by the headliner to do more than squeal, let alone order a plate of loaded potatoes or a Coke.

When I say "kiddie concert," I don't mean like a *baby show*; I mean a Teen Sensation Show. There are a lot of Teen Sensation Shows these days. New stars are being made every fifteen seconds or so online. When everyone was hanging out at home during Covid a couple years ago, there were two types of people: those who sat on their butts and watched Netflix (me), and those who went into overdrive, learned Sanskrit, composed songs, and choreographed elaborate dance maneuvers that they posted on TikTok. Anyway, the Teen Sensations are always very decent guests at the Lounge. They're still humble about their success, and well-aware of how brief it may be.

At least Dillon, the manager at the Lounge, scheduled Pat for the Back-of-House bar tonight, not the piddly little side-station that only sells beer and fountain drinks. At Back-of-House, Pat can pour well drinks, and maybe some shots. (Pat says that, with all the screaming kids, he figures *someone's* gonna need a shot.) That bar also has strategic placement: it's near both the merchandise area and the restrooms. Merch doesn't sell too much with the older crowds, but oh good lord, the teenagers *love* buying some swag. Will every little starry-eyed teeny-bopper want a commemorative tee shirt so they can re-live the magnificence of seeing their Teen Sensation idol perform Live?

"You betcha they will," Patrick told me, as I packed the car with cookies in the dark before dawn.

Not too long ago, Pat worked the Lounge when they had a Led Zeppelin tribute band from Omaha performing. Those old farts looked more likely to order lime Jell-O or play shuffleboard than swing into *Misty Mountain Hop*, Pat told me, laughing. Total bunch of geezers.

"But would you believe it? They rocked the house down. All these bald-ass, pot-bellied Boomers were shouting their heads off and drinking beer after beer." Pat laughed. "It was great."

My Patrick tends bar at the Camp Verde Lounge in Phoenix. It's about a fifteen hundred seat venue that gets the moderately popular acts. The

17

superstars, the Harry Styles or the U2 types, they all go the stadiums. And the rinky-dink acts that no one has heard of yet (and most likely never will) play at the bars off Mill Street at ASU or some of the bars in Mesa. Camp Verde Lounge is a huge step up from those dumps. The Lounge books its acts through Live Nation and Ticketmaster, not just some scruffy guy standing at the door grabbing cash.

I'm not just being snooty here to talk up Patrick; stronger ticket sales make for a longer lasting relationship with a venue. Sure, you don't get the kind of "regulars" you'd get at an actual bar, but then again, those come with their own sets of headaches. Drunks, sad sacks, brawls. You don't see those nearly as much when you bartend for the concert set. The sheer number of people in the crowd can get intimidating, Pat says, but the Lounge has its bars spaced pretty nicely throughout the space.

Tonight's concert is some cutie-pie girl singer whose amateur videos got downloaded about a million times or something when all the kids were at home quarantining. She was literally nobody just a year ago, just a pretty face with a guitar and an iPhone. The next thing you know, the kid's on a nationwide tour. Sure, she playing the Camp Verde Lounge and not Sun Devil Stadium, but it's still pretty remarkable when you think about it. Life can change pretty quickly when it wants to. I mean, she's the same age as my son. Except that Austin spent most of his quarantine time sleeping through his first year classes at U of A.

So while Patrick pours drinks for indulgent parents this weekend, I deal with the mix of tourists and locals at the Old Town Scottsdale Farmers Market. I even have a group of admirers, if you can believe that. These dudes think that, because I'm a woman and sitting by myself at my booth, I must be in desperate need of a man to chat me up. I'm cool with it, as long as they buy something. Most of them do, but not until after they complain that my stuff is overpriced. I very kindly do not tell them to stick my cookies up their tight asses. I smile and say, "It's the quality ingredients. They're made fresh and with love." I smile.

Today there is a slim gentleman with an impressive white mustache checking out the booth. He looks in great shape for a guy who appears to be in his eighties. Though with his suntan it's hard to tell. The snowbirds who come here get stupid-tan; after they hit about fifty years-old, they are all a uniform shade of mahogany. The slim gentleman has smile wrinkles around his eyes, which makes him look a bit more youthful. His dog (God, they always seem to bring a dog, but I am prepared with special pup cookies, made with peanut butter) is small, grey and shaggy.

"This is Wendy," he tells me, scratching the dog's ears. I hadn't asked.

"Thanks for visiting, Wendy," I respond. I am always nice to peoples' dogs. You learn to *never* be rude to anyone's dogs. Ever. People care more about their dogs than their kids around here. I'm not a huge dog person, but you'd never know it to hear me talk to these folks.

"You know. Like the song? The Bruce Springsteen song?"

I am absolutely blank for about ten seconds. Then: "Ha!" I slap my hand on the table. Now I like Mustache Guy and his shaggy dog, Wendy. "Do you have dreams and visions, sweetie?" I ask the dog, who cocks her head in that utterly adorable way some dogs do. *"Tramps like us,"* I sing, badly, loudly. *"Baby, we were born to run!"*

"You knew it!" Mustache guy cries.

"Greatest song ever written. What a great dog" Wendy smiles at me, her tongue lolling.

"She never bahks," the guy says. He has what I think is a thick Boston accent. "Since the day I first brought her home, she never bahks."

I'm in such a good mood after meeting Wendy and Mustache Guy that I don't even flip him off discreetly under the table when he leaves the booth without buying anything. Not even a little baggie of dog treats shaped like little bones and paw-prints.

There is a woman talking on her cellphone, which is funny because everybody just texts these days. She is clearly the type of gal who like to hear the sound of her own voice. Her shirt tells me that "Being a Mom is [Her] Superpower." She wears a tank top and leggings and must weigh all of a hundred and ten pounds. The sheer attitude it must have taken to get her body so tiny and fit is frankly intimidating. I try not to stare at her abs.

"I know!" she cries into her phone. "But I'm not going to respond her it. I'm not going down to

21

that level. You know, I'm a very spiritual person, so I can't engage with that kind of toxic energy."

There are quite a few *Spiritual People* in the Valley. I know this because their tee shirts announce it. They are *Spiritual Warriors*, in fact, and *Spiritual Gangster*, which is a bit more violent, but still intriguing. They have *Spirit Animals.*

One of my regulars, Curtis, says his apoplectic little Pomeranian is his spirit animal. Curtis must have a very neurotic spirit. The little yapper's name is *Nespa*, which is *Aspen* backwards. Aspen was his first Pomeranian. He has been dog-less the past week or two that I've seen him. Nespa has allergies, Curtis tells me. "She just hides in the closet and wheezes, poor little girl." He says.

"Aw, same here." I laugh. Curtis laughs too, and buys a couple cookies.

Today, I have prepared a batch of special cookies for my best friend Paula because it's her opening night. Paula does volunteer play-acting over at Rio Salado. A few times a year, they put on plays Paula's been involved with them for years. Paula likes to act, but doesn't always get the good roles because everything involved with community theater is super political, she tells me. The directors have their favorites, and cast them even if they are no good at all for the part. It's a shame; Paula would be very good in a big role. The cookies I made for her are shaped like stars and flowers. The stars say "Congrats!" and "Break A Leg!" The flowers are purple because Paula likes purple. I'll wait to go to see the play when I can go with Patrick, but I'll drop off the cookies at her condo so she can at least celebrate with a bite before and after the show.

Paula and I go way back, all the way to Coronado del Sol High School (Home of the Aztecs!) I guess it helps that we never moved too far away from where we grew up. But really, you'd think our friendship wouldn't have lasted, since our lives went in such different directions. Paula got pregnant our senior year at Coronado and got married to Josh the Asshole right after graduation. So she's already a grandmother, while my kid is still in college. I already told you about meeting Patrick. So, Paula left that dipshit Josh, then found *another* asshole a few years later and eventually she got rid of him too. She's had it rough; life can suck sometimes.

Paula's always wanted so much more than she's gotten. I think that's why she likes to mess around with that theater group. She wants to pretend to be someone else, and for a little while everything can be neat and clean. She's never actually *said* that to me, so maybe I'm just making stuff up. But it's nice to imagine that's why she does it. Paula's really fun to watch onstage because she can transform herself. You really believe that she is no longer Paula, the gal who used to work at the Dairy Queen with me after school, making those dipped cones.

One time, she played this tiny little part – just a busybody neighbor who tries to find out gossip about the handsome young drifter who's come into her small town. But she put it all out there. I believed she was that neighbor lady. Paula even did the role with a little bit of a cute Southern accent. It helps her forget that her son is out of work and that her daughter is mixed up with some asshole who spent time in jail for not paying child support, which is a major red flag if I've ever seen one. Paula's good people. I've packed up two dozen cookies for her. Retail value over forty dollars, but friends are worth going the extra mile for. Paula supported me after Mom died and I was going up and down an emotional roller coaster every other day. It's been a time.

*

My mother died in slow motion, in little pieces. Her heart was failing. Her kidneys were failing. She had cancer. What else? She was in her nineties. After a certain point in your late-eighties, pretty much everything starts to go. She was diminutive, diminished, but not dim. Never dim. I always said that Mom's tongue would still be flapping for weeks after they put her in the earth. Shooting out zingers about some liberal politician, or about how dumpy Barbra Streisand and Martha Stewart look without their makeup on.

I first knew Mom's end was imminent when she complimented how I looked when I visited. Does this sound cruel? It's not meant to be. My mama was many, many good things, but she was not kindly about my appearance. She had a mean streak that cosplayed as *concern for my health* and

25

a solicitous interest in my dating life. To her credit, she never gave me any shit about Patrick. But then again, Patrick *is* superhuman. Only a complete moron would ever say anything bad about my Pat. Other than he's too nice? That he settled for me? Big deal. That's not really insulting him.

But, yeah, my appearance. God, it drove Mom crazy. It might be my hair was too poofy or too flat, my pants were too tight, or that a pimple had unfortunately sprouted on my chin or nose. Mom was always crazy about those pimples. "Hey, you've got something on your face? Is that a bug bite? What's that on your nose?" Pretending not to know what it was. She played that game with me starting in my adolescence, and going all the way through to my fifties. She thought it was hilarious. I mean, even hearing myself say it now, it sounds kind of funny. Perspective is a wacky by-God thing to gain.

Another, a more chill, type of person would have laughed it off, made a joke about it, or simply let it roll off her back. I am not such a person. I internalize and store for later, self-soothing in my self-pity, waiting to spring it on Mom when we had one of our inevitable fights. The kind where both parties swear and bellow, then cry in each other's arms and have a drink, sniffling and licking our wounds.

So, like I said, I knew Mom was dying when she told me I looked good. Because I seriously was not. I'd put on a good ten pounds. I'd been avoiding visiting her once it got warmer because I knew she'd say something once it was short-sleeves weather. The woman was a bloodhound for extra pounds. Sometimes she'd pretend it was her own weight she worried about. Mom weighed about 135 soaking wet.

"Oh, I'd love to try those snickerdoodles you brought over, but I've been getting so *heavy* these past couple weeks." She'd say. "Why don't you wrap them up and I'll bring them to Bridge Club?"

Or this: "Let's walk a bit. I had some leftover carnitas enchiladas last night and I feel so bloated. I'll bet I gained three pounds overnight; I can hardly button my pants."

But by this time in her life, Mom wasn't up to taking her patented brisk walks up and down the sidewalks of her cute little subdivision of Los Ocotillos where all the other sassy old ladies in the

Valley seems to live. She wasn't up to much of anything them. Mom was so stooped by then that when she got up and walked she looked like a question-mark. This time, she took my hand and wheezed, "Hey, honey, you look beautiful. Come sit and talk." Ten days or so later, my fear was confirmed, and the next thing I knew I was trying to get clear the house of all her golf skirts, her collection of *Readers' Digest* magazines, and about nine hundred aloe plants in terra cotta pots.

Who in the world says that love is uncomplicated?

When someone you love dies, it's a horrible, enormous loss. The pain is tremendous and solid. And when that love has gone through literally decades of tension and tears and circumstances, the loss mutates into something else; it becomes a sad and terrible living creature. You can't just let it go; it gnaws at you. The screaming fights you used to have cannot be erased; they become muddy and sepia-toned. You start to question whether or not they even occurred. You never actually *forget* anything, but you feel guilty whenever an unattractive memory of the departed rears its head. You question yourself: why are you so petty to recall such negative moments? What kind of ingrate daughter are you? For God's sake, your mother died, you pathetic slob.

There will never really be absolute closure because one day you'll look in the mirror and notice how dumpy you've become in your matronly middle-age, and you'll hear your mother's voice from beyond the grave: "Maybe you should change slacks, Katherine. Ankle-length pants are better than capris because of where the hem hits you on the calf. The women in our family have terrible calves, you know. It's genetic."

And is that good or bad? I still haven't figured it out. Is it just my own terrible capacity for always seeing the worst in things? Or is it a good thing – like, I'm remembering her despite all her shortcomings, so it's sort of a little tribute? It annoys me that the voice I heard in my head is right about the stupid pants. And hilariously, the stupid voice is even doing to Mom-thing, saying *Katherine* instead of *Katie* to me because it disapproves.

Frankly, I prefer leggings. I wear leggings ninety-five percent of the time. But I *never* wore leggings when I visited my mother. And yes, I'm an adult with a son in college. Honestly, it was just not worth it. Life is too short to listen to Mom go on and on about how awful all women look in leggings. All while giving me a *look*.

Mom was an armchair matriarch who would probably go topless to the golf club before she'd squeeze herself into a pair of leggings. Cotton blouses and pantsuits, all the time, anytime. Unless it was linen. Linen might wrinkle easily, but it breathes nicely in this desert heat. Mom liked to hold court in her rattan chair on her patio, with her girlfriends around her, playing cards. She liked her chardonnay. And her margaritas. She didn't call them 'ritas, like everyone else in the Southwest; she called them *Margos*. As in, "Gail and I are having some *Margos* after golf." Or "The best *Margos* in town are at Roaring Fork, but only during their Happy Hour. I mean, who is going to pay full price for that?"

Mom was at her best when she was holding court over a roomful of admirers. For her eightieth birthday, a few years back, she had my brother and I organize a party in her honor. Not that we weren't going to do that already on our own, but Mom demanded it, told us who to invite (there was a lengthy list), what to serve (*Margos* were on the list), where to have it (McCormick Ranch Golf Club), and who was allowed to deliver a speech (my brother Jim, her sister Virginia, and her gentleman friend, Ed). I was not listed; I wouldn't have done it if she'd asked. I hate giving speeches. When I look back on it, though, it's probably because she didn't want to be embarrassed for me. Public speaking has never been my strength. I'm a blend-into-the-background kind of gal.

Unfortunately, this week my tendency to be reserved bit me in the ass big time today because somehow Angela talked me into going to one of those crazy psychics she's so into. She does this once every couple months. There is an abundance of psychics in this area because the desert is supposed to be mystical or something. People around here are really into wacky things like driving out to the MacDowell or Superstition Mountains at sunset so they can to *feel the energy* of nature. And then they do yoga moves on the rocks. The sunsets in this area are pretty fantastic, I admit. Every night is a showstopper. Every. Night. The mountains become purple and the sky is lavender fading into indigo. The clouds are cotton candy pink, ringed in yellow. Then the lights of the Valley start twinkling. It actually looks fake, like someone painted it.

"Sunsets are a Spiritual Thing," says Angela. And she should know because her name has "angel" in it, right? Angela says that the spirits are *called to this area* because of the landscape. "You can feel them," she says.

But, let's say you're a ghost, right? Do you really care about scenery in the physical world now that you've passed on? Why do you want to hang out specifically in the desert, pretty sunsets or not? Wouldn't it be just as easy to hang out in Dubuque or Hoboken? Do ghosts maybe just like it really dry? When you think about it, you're kind of insulting all the ghosts who just happen to live in places like Atlanta or Detroit.

The psychic Angela found this time is supposed to be more authentic because she's just a person; she doesn't work out of some cheesy storefront out in Old Town for the tourists, with piped in flute music and crystals. This one is supposedly part Yavapai and lives out on Osborne near that dumpy Agave Springs Nursing Home. So we drive out together to this woman's place to appease Angela.

The psychic, Raina something, is a pretty sixtyish-looking lady with short salt and pepper hair. I was kind of expecting her to wear a veil or a turban or something, but she looked like anybody you might run into in the deli section at Albertsons any given morning. Raina works out of her apartment, which is an absolutely nondescript building of fake adobe with sun shades in the parking lot and a pool in the back, like a thousand others in the neighborhood. She has some gorgeous purple prickly pear cacti alongside the entryway to her place.

We sit down in her perfectly normal family room. No incense, no crystal ball. Lots of light, in fact. I can hear a dog whining from the kitchen. Raina offers us water; Angela says yes, so I do too.

"Does the noise bother you?" she asks. "Sorry, we just adopted a puppy."

We tell her it's no big deal, that we love dogs.

I feel like we're here for a book club meeting, and not a spiritual quest. I give Angela a raised eyebrows *look* when Raina is getting our waters. Angela ignores me.

"Alrighty, let's get settled," says Raina, after finishing her drink. She sits up straighter and smooths down her skirt. I guess we're really going to do this.

Raina takes a deep breath, then says, "So, is there someone who has passed over that you wish to contact?"

"Yes." We both pipe up.

Angela can't help herself; she has to spill everything. "My Aunt Trudie. She passed on right after the New Year."

I am not going to tell this woman a damned thing. If she's for real, then I won't have to. But she's not real because life doesn't work like that. You don't always get what you want. But I am not giving an inch; let's see her work.

"I should tell you ladies a little about myself before we get started, should I?" says Raina. "I've always been able to speak with the angels. When I was a little girl, I thought everyone could see them. It wasn't until I mentioned the *Pretty People* to my parents that I realized I wasn't like other kids. Of course, then my parents thought I was mentally ill. In fact, I was sent to psychiatrists, therapists, social workers from the time I was eight years old." I really wish I could poke Angela or something right now, but it would be too obvious to the psychic. This story is something else. Raina continues:

"I've learned throughout my years of speaking to those who have passed that they are not quite the same as they were on the earthly plane. So you cannot expect the exact same kind of communication. They are usually still getting used to be on the Other Side. I go by feelings, and I can sense what they want to convey. Do you understand?"

We agree.

"There is a presence standing over your right shoulder, Angela. And she is smiling at you." I keep my face impassive. Angela eats it up.

"Is it Aunt Trudie?" she asks. She has tears in her eyes.

"It's a female presence who loves you very much." says the psychic. "She wants you to know that she is always with you, and that she loves you very much. She is sending you signs that she is nearby. Little coins that you will find, maybe on the sidewalk, or at the bottom of your purse when you don't expect them. And a rainbow, from time to time. Those are her signs that she loves you and is watching over you."

Angela is now sobbing, "I love you, Aunt Trudie. We all miss you so much. I hope it wasn't too rough on you at the end."

"She says that all her pain is behind her now," Raina intones. Then she turns to me. "I sense someone around you. A loving presence." I keep my silence.

"Oh, Katie, it's your mother!" pipes up Angela. Great. Thanks, Einstein. This, of course, gets Raina going.

"Your mother, yes. She is standing over your right shoulder right now, and she is stroking your hair. She says to tell you that she loves you very much and is watching over you. She tells me that she sends you little reminders of her presence, usually a bird. She sends you birds."

"Oh, that's nice," I say.

Death must certainly change people quite a bit because my mother had a decades' long feud with the grackles in her neighborhood. She hated those "little bastards" as she called them. It was pretty hilarious. Grackles do have beady little eyes, and their cries are kind of mean. Mom didn't mind the hummingbirds or quails, though. I mean, even my mother could see that they're adorable. But Mom was not a Bird Lady, not by a long shot.

In fact, she used to make special trips out to Scottsdale Avian Solutions to get special *bird-be-gone* custom screens for her solar panels and chimney pipe. She sprayed Bird-X on her lemon tree. The starlings drove her crazy, crapping on her nice stone pavers. And don't even get me started on the Canadian geese that frequented the pond in her neighborhood, the slimy green cylinders of their turds dotting the sidewalks.

"Ok, then," I say. "I'll keep an eye out for birds."

I picture Mom, not as she was before she died, but in her feistier times. There is literally no way in a million years that she would stand behind me and stroke my hair. She'd punch me in the shoulder and tell me to get off my duff and put on some flattering clothes instead of this dumpy tee-shirt.

Driving home, I feel a weird mixture of vindication and disappointment. I knew they wouldn't be able to talk to Mom. I *knew* it. But still. I think of how Mom would've laughed at that psychic gal, with her round pale face and her stupid incense. Did Raina think Mom was Snow White or something, befriending all the little woodland creatures from the Great Beyond? I snort, thinking of Mom with a *Margo* clutched in one knobby hand, while a mourning dove perched on the other.

These psychics all say the same thing. "They're happy. They're sending you their love." Like death is some sort of command message center of good will. Anyway, these people are fucking ghouls, just taking advantage of grieving people. It made Angela feel better, though. Good for her. I am at least a supportive friend, if a hypocritical one.

It's getting on in the afternoon when I pull into our driveway. Pat's Camry is still in the garage, which is odd because normally he's out the door well before four. He likes to spend plenty of time setting things up behind the bar. Maybe he got a call from his brother and lost track of time. Pat has a brother out in New Jersey, and the two of them can talk like a couple of old ladies. Hours long conversations, laughing, giving each other no end of shit. It's fun to watch. I never really had that same kind of relationship with my brother, but these two are like twins. They're Irish twins anyway, ten months apart. Pat and Rick are basically the same person, same dark brown hair and eyes, same build, same chicken legs. It's adorable to see them together. We don't get out to Jersey nearly as much as we should, but every now and then the two of them go out to Vegas together for a weekend of heavy drinking and poker tournaments. Pat always comes back home a few hundred dollars poorer but the tales he weaves are worth it. And he looks perkier. Funny how a weekend of booze and eating like crap can rejuvenate someone, but there you have it.

"Hey baby, what's up?" I call from the kitchen. "When are you taking off?"

And there's Pat, sitting on the floor of our bathroom. It's his stomach again. This happens fairly frequently. Pat eats something stupid (like hot wings; he loves those stupid hot wings) and then suffers for a day or two while they work their way out of his system. But I think they're giving him an ulcer. I mean, the man's in his fifties; he can't go around eating and drinking like he's in high school forever. I get him some Tums and help him into bed. He's already called off from work so I know that his time it's serious.

"Jesus, Pat, you've got to lay off all the spicy stuff." I tell him.

"Katie, we live in the Southwest. What else is there to eat?" he kind of grimaces when he speaks. I give him milk, but he won't drink it. His face is flushed. But then again, he's Irish. His face always looks a little ruddy. It's a nasty bout of indigestion.

"No more wings. No more going to Los Dos Molinos for those crazy hot burritos." Pat laughs.

I left the kitchen a disaster area, which is par for the course. There are pans and mixing bowls and bags of icing everywhere. I start the long haul clean up.

"Hey, Kate?" I turn off the hot water and dry my hands. There's Pat. He's put on some sweat pants and shoes. He's standing soft of slumped over, like it hurts to straighten up. "Take me to Urgent Care, ok, Baby?"

We go to Fast Med Urgent Care on Southern and wait, wait, wait for a Physician Assistant to check Pat out. They take his blood pressure, his temperature, they prod his belly and his back, they ask about his medical history. They don't think it is indigestion. They give us directions to Banner Urgent Care over on McClintock because Pat needs an MRI. This Urgent Care gives Pat a hefty dollop of drugs to stop his pain. The MRI results are not good. A pleasant-looking young Latina tells me matter-of-factly that Pat needs to be admitted—now -- into Honor Health Deer Valley Medical Center on 27th street. It appears that my Patrick has a case of diverticulitis with a large abscess in the wall of his colon. They've already called the hospital to let them know we're coming. He's going to need surgery. I try to talk to Pat to figure out what's going on, but he is already loopy from the drugs.

"Yeah, they got me some sweet pain meds," Pat slurs. "I can sleep in the car on the way home, ok?"

"You're not going home, big guy," I tell him.

The nice young lady explains to me that diverticula are tiny little fissures in the wall of Pat's colon. Stuff sometimes gets stuck in the pockets, and sometimes the colon doesn't like that and it gets all irritated and forms an abscess. In worse scenarios, sometimes the abscess gets *crazy-*irritated and ruptures. And when that happens, it means that the waste product (this is their polite medical way of saying *shit*) that normally travels happily through your colon can be rudely exposed to the rest of your abdominal cavity. Which can result in sepsis. Oh, my God.

I drive Pat to Deer Valley, where he is again poked and prodded and hooked up to an impressive amount of tubes. He has a morphine drip going. For a tall man, Pat looks tiny and vulnerable there on the hospital bed. The room is far too warm. I'm sweating buckets, but I guess the intravenous drip makes Pat cold, so we keep the room warm. I'm frantically texting Paula to tell her about the situation, then I remember that it's her opening night at Rio Salado, and she has probably put her phone away. I'm not really in the mood to text Angela, but I do anyway. She responds that she is praying for Pat. I hadn't thought of Pat are requiring prayers, so Angela's message gives me a cold chill, even in this tropical room.

I craft a careful text message to Austin, trying to sound like I'm not panicking and that everything is serious, but nothing to worry about, certainly he shouldn't drive up here from Tucson until we know more. Austin is a good kid, but he needs every spare moment to knuckle down on his classes. He might be so crazy as to use this as an opportunity to drop a class, telling the administrative Powers That Be that his father is going through a medical emergency. That would be just like Austin, wouldn't it? Finding a way to get out of a test or two.

I speak to the surgeon, Dr. Debarros, who is a very serious-looking guy with *a basso profundo* voice and wavy black hair. He seems absolutely humorless, which is both comforting and terrifying.

Debarros says that yes, Pat's condition is serious; the abscess may rupture. But I am not to worry because this sort of situation is Debarros' specialty. He's going to operate on Pat, but he can't because his colon is currently "too hot." Going in there while the infection is raging will piss off all the other organs down there, is the sense I'm getting.

We wait three days. Pat, on a Clear Liquids Only diet (chicken broth and Jell-O), wastes away to nothing before my eyes. I joke to him that I'd love to have his weight-loss regime. The minute I leave the hospital, I hit the 24 hour drive-through at Filiberto's. I don't even have time to hate myself; I'm worrying too hard.

Austin drives up from school, looking like a college student: disheveled and unshaven. His eyes are glassy. We go to the hospital together. He gets Pat to laugh, telling funny stories about his professors and his fraternity brothers. It's good to see Pat smiling; he's been so quiet with me. For someone as buoyant as Pat, it's spooky to see him withdrawn. Of course, he's on a diet of pretty crazy strong antibiotics, to take down the infection going on in his nether regions.

Pat and Austin make poop jokes so vulgar that they make even me blush, and I've got a pretty high tolerance. That kid, he's crazy. Austin kisses my cheek when he leaves the hospital to catch up on some sleep. And that adult gesture made by my baby boy makes me tear up.

I worried about Austin so profoundly for so many years that it's hard to comprehend that I'm not worrying about him right now. Seriously, there are problematic kids, and then there's Austin. It's been that way since he gave me Morning Sickness for six months straight, before he even took a breath of air. He was colicky from day one. And a picky eater. Oh, he made my life a living Hell for years, that kid. And then he would giggle and hug me and all was forgotten, but oh, golly, what a bumpy ride that was.

I constantly compared myself to other mothers whose babies sat up, crawled, spoke, and used a potty-seat before he did. I remember how I used to think: *if only he can go one day without wetting his pants during preschool, then I'll never ask for anything ever again.* That's a laugh riot now, isn't it? Or when he was in Elementary School: *for the love of God, please let him make some friends and be happier.* Or high school: *Please let him come home safely.* It never ends. But oh, golly, thanks goodness he's only a couple hours' drive away; I think I'd actually implode otherwise.

Mom very helpfully told me that neither my brother Jim nor I ever acted the way Austin did as a baby, and that his behavior was probably due to all the antibiotics they feed to cows, which makes their milk become all messed up. Not that Austin was a big milk-drinker; he loved apple juice, though. Mom spoiled him rotten, which also probably explains a lot. I always felt like she was judging my parenting. Pat would tell me to chill and get some rest. Pat was right. Pat's always been right.

You worry about your baby, then your little boy, then your young man. And then surprise: you get to worry about your husband! Full circle. And lucky you, in between all that, you get to worry about your parents. First one, then the other. When one worry starts to slowly ebb away, the next one rears its ugly damned head. And it's your own steadily rising blood pressure looming on the horizon. At my last check-up, they put me on

Metoprolol. Fabulous. But it's not me lying there on the bed, it's Pat. The guy I've never once in twenty-one years ever worried about. Not about his love for me or his commitment to our little family or his willingness to be in this for the long haul. That's pretty remarkable. I'm a lucky woman.

Pat is prepped for surgery before seven am, surgery scheduled for eight. I am not even to bother coming in to the hospital until he's in recovery. Surgery is delayed for a couple hours for some reason. It is late afternoon and I have eaten about six sugar cookies and three cupcakes when I finally get a call from the surgical nurse, Hannah, who tells me that Pat is resting comfortably. I can come see him in an hour or so.

His poor hair is all matted and flattened onto his scalp. He looks oddly bloated. They have removed twelve inches – one foot! – of Pat's colon. He is barely coherent. He asks for some water. I bring him a cup and he sips through the straw. I stay in the room until visiting hours are up, even though Pat starts snoring pretty steadily. The familiar buzz he makes is heartbreaking out of context. I want to make sure that all the machines he's hooked up to keep beeping steadily. I want the silent, competent nurses to reassure me that his recovery will be easy. Everything seems to be working nicely. I call Austin and tell him that Dad's going to be just fine in a few days. He will need to get his strength back after eating nothing all week. He will have to eat very carefully, though. I tell him about the twelve inches of colon and even Austin is impressed.

"Holy shit," he says. "Damn."

Paula texts me and says she's baked a lasagna for Austin and me. Just what I need, ha ha, but of course I thank her. Cassie, my assistant at the Flour Shop has been working like a demon while I've been gone. She says that she and June will take care of the Farmers Market this weekend.

I leave the hospital and head for my car. Even in the fading light, I can tell that I made a rookie mistake in the parking lot. In my haste to get in and check on Pat, not only did I neglect to park under one of the numerous sun-shade areas, but I compounded my error by parking directly under a tree. My nice car is absolutely covered in bird crap. The hood and roof are splattered with white-grey nasty goo. I can picture the birds perching in the branches, all afternoon and into the evening, just letting loose on my poor car for hours. Suddenly I'm shaking and snorting with laughter. And then the tears of relief start in, so before long I'm all snotty and gross and out of breath and shaking with laughter. I'm still smiling when I get home for the night.

JACKRABBIT DREAMS

I'm Mr. Loverman, and I miss my lover, man

They've seated me another bachelorette party at Table 14. The second one I've had tonight. I know they are a bachelorette party because it's a party of eight females in their mid-to-late twenties, all dressed in identical pink tank tops with *"I Do Crew"* emblazoned across the chest. As if that were not enough to distinguish them, one of the *I Do Crew* is wearing a headband that has tiny little penises dangling off it like unfortunate insect antennae. Because it is now after 6:00 pm, I'm guessing these girls ("*women*"—*yes, Molly, I'm displaying my latent sexism*) have been pre-gaming for hours already. Each and every one of these women is crazily, painfully beautiful.

They all came in on one of the numerous Party Bikes that pass through here. For the uninitiated, the Party Bike is a bicycle built for up to fifteen. It's sort of a bike attached to a large cart, seating eight along each side. The riders face inwards, and have a small shade above their heads, that doesn't shade much more than the drinks. There are built in cup-holders on the cart, and a cooler in the center. Each rider pedals from their seat, with a Party Bike Captain steering. For $50 per person, or $499 for the whole bike, you can spend an evening rolling slowly through the streets of Old Town, sipping White Claw and playing Shania Twain music.

It's a Scottsdale tradition these days. The bikes take a leisurely "pub crawl," wherein the riders (almost exclusively female; I honestly have never seen any men on these things except for the "captains" who steer them) scream and wave at the tourists on the sidewalks, who laugh and take photos of them. Then they stop in at one of their "Partner Bars," (El Mescal is a proud Party Bike Partner!) for some indoor drinking, before hopping aboard once again. I've been told that the Party Bikes will start roaming the streets as early as 9:30 am. They don't do the pub crawls then, obviously, because nothing is opened except the brunch places and coffee shops. But you can stock the bike with booze (as long as it's purchased from the Party Bike Store, and not brought in on your own!) and just peddle to your heart's content. The daylight riders tend to get sunburned on their backs. I shouldn't make fun; it's a living for those drivers. It could easily be me driving one of those contraptions. There, but for the grace of God, go I.

Table 14 is *loud* -- if by "loud," one really means that the sound of this bunch makes my teeth hurt. And that's *over* the techno playlist we play here at El Mescal, the bass notes throbbing from four to midnight, the synth buzzing like a worrisome memory. I know all about worrisome memories these days, but I also know about Moving On.

Moving On means I go to work at El Mescal four shifts a week and smile charmingly for all the bachelorette parties and after-work get-togethers that involve tequila shots and the occasional bucket of our (admittedly, quite tasty) Loco Wings. It helps pay the bills, which are a significantly higher now that I live alone.

El Mescal is one of several bars in Old Town Scottsdale that is popular because it stands on some prime real estate. Location is everything. People will buy our overpriced cocktails because El Mescal is cool and therefore the cool people want to drink here. We are *never* not-packed, just like Loco Patron and Diego Pops nearby. We don't get the families, though we do occasionally get older gentlemen on the prowl. We are just off the canal, a short walk away from the intersection Scottsdale Road and Camelback.

To be a server here, you need to be quick on your feet, thick-skinned, and good at reading lips. The music is always too loud and the people are generally beautiful. You might not believe it, but the food is also excellent, if you've not completely burned out your palate with alcohol. El Mescal only opened here nine months ago, but already we have built up a healthy, if perpetually drunk and frequently belligerent, clientele.

The group at Table 14 has not ordered Loco Wings; they've not ordered any food, which does not bode well for their well-being tomorrow. They have, however, ordered their second round of shots, which I distribute around the table, to the accompaniment of their cheers. The dark-haired one, the one sitting next to the BRIDE-TO-BE (as emblazoned on her tank top), has grabbed my ass twice now, or at least tried. I managed to sidle away from her a bit, so she ended up grabbing at my leg instead. The rest of the party notices and whoops enthusiastically.

"Cheers, ladies. Are we ready to order?" I smile, distributing shot glasses.

"Don't do that, Emma!" The one with the penis headband shouts to her grabby friend. Maybe she will be the nice one in this crew, I think. Then she adds: "He's not on our team" in a loud stage whisper.

The rest of the party shushes her, worried about offending me, which is considerate. Later on in the evening, when things really start getting crazy, all niceties will likely disappear, and I will be treated any way the customer likes. Like I said, it pays the bills.

I am often mistaken for being gay here at the restaurant. Because I am a server at a hipster place and because I am skinny and relatively well-groomed. But mostly because my voice is not deeply masculine. Molly used to call me "her little twink." And I didn't even mind; in fact, it drove me crazy. But then again, everything about Molly drove me crazy, even her casual little cruelties. God, I miss her.

Being mistaken for a homosexual can often be advantageous in a place like El Mescal. The female customers feel they can confide in you, and the gay men flirt outrageously with you. The aggressively masculine cowboy types don't tend to frequent El Mescal, preferring instead the many local brewpubs or places like Senor Agave's, where they can get deals on pitchers of Four Peaks. They'll take their dates to El Mescal, but they don't hunt here in packs; it's a bit of a truce.

I'm actually grateful that I have this job at El Mescal. The constant noise and movement and short-term memory nature of this job gets me out of my own head. When I am back at home, writing music and playing guitar, all I think about is the broken remains of my post-Molly existence. It's made for some pretty cool, melancholy songs, though. Rory keeps insisting I switch it around and write something cheerful for a change. Instead, I play the same old sad songs, but with a jauntier, more upbeat sound. People don't always listen to the words; first impressions come from the feel of the music.

Bachelorette Party Season is in full throttle here in Old Town. The entire Greater Phoenix Metropolitan Area is inundated with toxic, tipsy herds of Bridesmaids. The bachelor parties mostly go to Vegas these days, for a weekend of gambling and debauchery, whereas the girls (*women, dammit!*) come to the Valley of the Sun for a Spa weekend laced with tequila shots. The younger bachelorettes add in horseback rides, while the older ones seem to favor golf outings. When you live here long enough, you really start to see the migratory patterns.

My Table 14 bachelorette party sensibly decides to order some appetizers. I recommend the Javelina Poppers and Fusion Nachos. The dark-haired grabber of asses tells me that she'll take whatever I bring her, so I smile my brightest and thank her, dashingly raising my eyebrows, while the rest of the party hoots. The BRIDE TO BE looks slightly shiny; the tequila shots may have been too much for her. Not my problem; the bride never pays for this evening out. I need to keep track of the penis headband girl (*woman!*); she looks moderately responsible, maybe enough to be the Maid of Honor, headgear notwithstanding.

*

Everything started with Juno. It's true. If she hadn't run out of the apartment one morning – out of the blue – my life would be on a completely different trajectory right now. Juno and I met up a couple years ago, when Rory and I were rooming together. The lady upstairs from us owned a cat that had kittens, and Rory thought it might be nice to have a little pet. She was the tiniest little thing, all fluffy and squeak-meowing, falling asleep in my lap. You kind of have to have a heart of stone to not fall in love with a kitten.

Rory named her Juno after the Greek Queen of the Gods, which is a perfect name for her. Some people think cats are stand-offish, but not Juno. She thrives on petting and affection, always wanting to be the center of attention. She purrs like a freight train and curls into a giant orange fluff-ball when she sleeps. Her only fault is a compulsion to knock items off shelves or counter-tops. She honestly can't stop herself: if there is a glass or a pen or a pair of glasses on a table top, Juno will gently bat at it with her little orange and white paws till it crashes to the floor. Rory and I loved getting Juno stoned with catnip, and making her run around like a nut, chasing a flashlight beam.

Which is why it was so totally shocking when she ran off. We'd had her for a couple years already; she was a fully grown, spayed adult cat. Not the likely type to roam. Rory was going out to buy groceries or something; he opened our front door, and out dashed Juno. She'd never done this before, never even seemed to want to explore the outside at all, beyond a keen fascination with the birds and lizards that occasionally zipped by our windows.

"I'm sure she'll come home again, soon." Rory kept saying. "She can't go without her Friskies Beach Party Treats for more than a day."

But Juno stayed away. After four days, we made signs and plastered them up and down Baseline Road, at gas stations, the antiques mall, all the apartment complexes, and at the Frye's on McClintock: "Have you seen this cat?" With a very nice photograph of Juno curled up in a sunbeam.

"Juno is a three year-old, very affectionate orange tabby. She will answer to her name, but has all her claws, so be careful! Please do not chase! Last seen at Camelot Apartments on February 4th." At the bottom of the signs, we listed both of our cell phone numbers.

No response for ten days, and then Juno showed up, yowling at the front door in the middle of the night. Looking absolutely unscathed, as if she'd been sleeping on someone's couch, not roughing it on the mean streets of Tempe for two weeks, battling rats and scorpions, no doubt. As Rory stood in the doorway gaping, Juno ran between his feet, through the hall and into my bedroom, where she hid under the bed and didn't come out till the middle of the next day. She didn't even investigate the tuna we optimistically left out for her every day. Rory speculated that Juno may have been dumpster diving; how else was she not ravenous? We took her to Topaz Veterinary Clinic, where the staff found our kitty to be in perfect health.

Rory and I were so delighted with Juno's unexpected return that we never bothered to take down the posters. Also we are basically lazy slobs, if you must know the truth. At any rate, Juno had been home for a couple weeks when I got a call from an unknown number. I let it go to voicemail. The voice on the message was light and a little sing-song-y, with the ghost of a country accent.

"Hello? I'm calling to tell you I saw your poster about your missing cat? I haven't seen her, sorry. But I just wanted to let you know how sad I am that your friend ran away. Also, I'm really getting a vibe that your Juno has not been killed or hurt. I definitely think she will come home to you soon. Keep your eyes and ears open. She loves you and wants to come home. Have a beautiful day. Bye."

Of course, I had to call back and tell the mystery voice that Juno *had* in fact returned home. And that was how I met Molly. She of the elaborate eye make-up and porcelain skin. Lover of turquoise jewelry and Sonoran hot dogs and weekend trips to Sedona to hike the vortices. Living embodiment of every imaginable carnal (or spiritual) fantasy. My lady, my muse. Breaker of hearts.

Molly has strawberry blond hair that she braids like Laura Ingalls Wilder in two thick ropes down her shoulders. Her nose is dusted with freckles. She is small and compact; when she sits cross-legged, she looks like you could fit her in your backpack. She likes to wear overall shorts with a tank top and hiking boots. Molly buys raw wool and dyes it with materials like onion skins and marigolds. She then spins it herself and creates funky, textured wall-hangings she tries to sell at Salt Flats Dry Goods and Mountain Thyme Gift Shop, places that support local artisans.

Molly has a tattoo on the inside of her right forearm: a tiny heart with a peace sign inside it. Her eyes are blue and sometimes grey and sometimes almost green, depending on her emotional radar. She'll tell you right away that she's a Gemini, a double-spirit. If she had called Rory's number instead of mine, what would have happened? What if I had simply deleted the message? How can something as earth-shattering as our meeting have been left to chance?

Molly came to Arizona from Reno, with aspirations of becoming a textile artist. She is amazingly talented, and it's unfortunate that the rest of the world isn't as receptive of her gifts as they should be, so Molly flits between jobs. Sometimes she works the Arizona Renaissance Festival or the Spa at the Gainey Ranch Hyatt, or at Renegade Coffee Shop. Other time, she helps out with costuming stuff for local theater companies or teaches children's art classes. She can point out all the major constellations. Molly is the most singular person I've ever encountered. She contains multitudes; she defies logic; she beggars all description.

Molly has another name, *Thomasin*. She picked it out from some movie about a witch. Of course. It is her *true name*, the name of her essence, Molly told me. She uses it when she works the Renaissance Festival. "You have a true name too, Ben," she would say to me. "But you haven't found it yet. Keep looking and it will come to you." And I'd look into those kohl-rimmed eyes and forget that I even had a name, let alone something truer than Ben Gibley, formerly of Peoria, Arizona, now merely a shell of a former human being, currently existing in Tempe.

I may not know my *true* name yet, but I do have a nickname. My sister and her kids call me "Eubie," which is short for Uncle Ben (get it? U.B.?). They also occasionally call me Minute Rice (see what they did there?). Molly loved that, and would sometimes call me Minute Rice as a sexy kind of joke. Or maybe it was just sexy to me? Or maybe I am misremembering again. Rory tells me I tend to embellish the past with Molly, "gilding your memories" he says. But honestly, I can't remember anything negative about Molly. Except of course that she left me.

My dad, now he would tell you a different story. He seems to think that Molly holds some sort of responsibility for me not pursuing a lucrative career as a dermatologist or a claims adjuster or an astronaut. The truth of the matter is that I had stopped taking classes full-time at ASU long before I met Molly. Was I attracted to Molly because she is a free spirit? No doubt. But if I had told her I was quitting music (and by extension, waiting tables) forever and becoming a stock broker, she would have been cool with that. That's how Molly is.

My dad wants me to be *comfortable*. Which means he wants me to have a normal nine-to-five job that doesn't depend on tips and the kindness of intoxicated Bridesmaids. He wants me to be like my sister Lynn, who is only two years older than me, but has a BA (in sensible Accounting), a husband, a house in Mesa and two daughters, ages three and five.

My nieces *loved* Molly; even Lynn could see how sweet they were together. Molly would make them friendship bracelets out of wildly colored embroidery floss, and braid their hair and play with them like a little kid, not an uptight adult. Molly and

I went to the girls' soccer games and ballet recitals too. Sometimes I think that Lynn never completely warmed to Molly because she suspected that Molly might be my Forever Person. And if that happened, I'd be having a family of my own and Lynn would lose Eubie the Fun Uncle. But again, I'm probably just being bitter. Of course I still go, all by my lonesome now, to see the girls' games and all. I think Lynn warns them not to ask me anything about Molly because they never mention her name. It's kind of sad, really.

My mom, on the other hand, just wants me to settle down. In the eyes of God, that is. Or even a Justice of the Peace; Mom's getting desperate. She wants more grandchildren and she wants them yesterday. I don't think she'd even care if I was still slinging tequila over at El Mescal, as long as I had a wife and kids to call my own. So you can see: I'm getting a bit of conflicting signals from my immediate family.

Of course, waiting tables doesn't define me. It's a side-gig. Practically every server in the history of time has a Real Career they are pursuing, be it getting through law school, acting, supporting a troublesome gambling addiction, modeling (one guy and two girls here at El Mescal are –legit -- models; the rest of us kind of hate them for the tips they get), or plain old run of the mill musicians like me. I, like so many before me, am awaiting my First Big Break. I had thought that I was awaiting it with Molly, but fate has it in for me lately.

After Molly left, my dad stopped by my (no longer "our") apartment under the pretense of dropping off a pan of tamales my mom had made. I hadn't gotten out of bed in two days then, except to grab another beer. I'd been playing Radiohead tunes like "Karma Police" on repeat for about two hours, so my melancholy and anguish were downright palpable by that point. The apartment must have smelled like the devil's armpit. Dad put the foil-wrapped pan on the counter and sat down on the sofa. His forced smile was almost as pathetic as my existential despair.

"So? What's new? You seem a little down, Ben."

He meant well. We tiptoed around the elephant in the room and talked about the upcoming holidays. Would I be spending Christmas

Eve with him and Mom? Was there anything special on my wish list? Our visit ended with Dad leaving me a list of job openings he'd copied down from somewhere online. It was such a sweet gesture that I didn't even give him a hard time for not merely *sending me* the link. The guy wanted an excuse to see for himself how badly I was doing. I assured him I'd look into the job leads, and Dad lit up with relief, but of course I never did. We haven't talked much since Christmas.

I'm a disappointment.

*

The woman at Table 14 who is probably the Maid of Honor comes through for the group, figuring out everyone's share of the bill (which El Mescal will not split, since they are a party of more than five) – except the BRIDE TO BE, of course. She tips me, if not handsomely, at least not insultingly low either. The BRIDE TO BE is well on her way to a magnificent hangover tomorrow, leaning sloppily on her bridal party friends as they exit the restaurant.

The bussers descend upon Table 14 to clear the plates and glasses. Mackinley, tonight's Hostess, is already eyeballing my section while talking to another large group. It's the Circle of Life, folks. I notice that the newish guy, Zach, battles with a feral bachelorette party in his section as well. This group is distinguished by their matching pink tee shirts, the bride with a veil that dangles dangerously askew from a comb on the crown of her head.

Zach is in danger of losing his cool with these ladies; he has not quite yet tuned into the vibe here at El Mescal. I see that frozen grimace, jaw-clenched tension in his face, which is getting redder as I watch him. His hair, longish, kind of cool, starts sticking to the sides of his face. Poor guy. He's a kid, though. Maybe all of twenty-two?

I help Zach by running food to his other tables while he contends with the Bachelorettes. Mackinley has not yet seated Table 14, so I'm momentarily at a lull. My other three tables are all deuces, couples on dates. I can tell from the way that they are all paying rapt attention to each other that none of these folks are married. Not one of them is looking at their phone, and that's six people total! Maybe they are all having affairs? It's astonishing to see that kind of attention span these days.

*

"Marriage ruins everything," Molly used to tell me. "Marriage destroys love by commodifying it into a State Construct. I don't need the government to sanction how I love."

"That's cool, baby," I'd tell her. "Just don't say that in front of my mom." And Molly would laugh and kiss me.

When Molly works the Renaissance Festival on winter weekends out by Apache Junction, she is stuck being a barmaid at the Tudor Rose Pub. That's the one that's near the Middleshire Stage where the Fairhaven Morris Dancers perform. She fills flagons of lager (otherwise known as Miller High Life) all day long, with a purple and pink flowered wreath in her hair. She wears a period costume she made herself (of course); her hair is intricately braided and piled on her head. The other Festival employees all look like sad sacks playing dress-up, but Molly *embodies* her role. At the Tudor Rose, she only answers to *Thomasin*. She would dearly love to get her own booth and sell handmade clothing there, kirtles and bodices with trumpet sleeves and doublets for the men. But the competition to get a spot there is huge, and the organization has their favorites, and of course you have to pay.

I visited Molly at the Festival, naturally, buying an enormous turkey leg and finding a shady spot near Storybook Castle (the kiddie play-area), so I could sit and watch Molly work. It's actually a great place to sit and think and maybe jot down new song lyrics. A little bit of Merry Olde England just East of the greater Phoenix area. Molly says the only thing she dislikes about the Festival is having to take her nose piercing out.

"I'm willing to bet that there were plenty of pierced noses in the Renaissance," she pouted. "Shakespeare had a pierced ear, for Christ's sake."

Molly felt very deeply about her nose-piercing. It went right through her septum, like a ring on a bull. But Molly's jewelry was a delicate sterling silver bar with tiny round knobs at the end, dainty, almost feminine. Septum piercings are important, she told me. They strengthen your ovaries. I most certainly did argue with her on that one.

So besotted was I with Molly and her magic, I even sent out an application for next season to be one of the traveling troubadours who wander around the fairgrounds. That way, Molly and I could be actual co-workers. I'd have to play a mandolin and not my guitar, but it'd be totally worth it.

For a little while, last year, through a connection of Rory's, I got a couple gigs playing at local weddings. Whenever they needed a vocalist, I pulled Molly in. She has a light, breathy soprano with a touch of vibrato. She sounds like a Ren Faire Girl, like her name really *could be* Thomasin, if that makes any sense. Like she'd be happy just singing *Greensleeves* and *Come Away, Sweet Love Doth Now Invite* over and over again till doomsday. Some days, I'd get out my acoustic guitar and just strum away while Molly's little light voice trilled and the scented candles burned down to the nubs – until one of us broke the spell by having to leave for a paying job. It was bliss.

I know I sound like I'm making this up about how awesome Molly and I were together, but it's true, all of it. It was that kind of happiness that transcends reality. Where physical and metaphysical are one and the same. The kind of love that only comes once in a lifetime and you need to take immediate advantage of, before you start to think about it too clearly because that might spoil the magic.

Case in point: Molly and I used to hike together. We'd leave before sunrise and drive out to South Mountain or Lost Dog Wash or Tom's Thumb. Even in the summertime, when any time after about eight am meant you were in the eighties. For someone so tiny, Molly is wiry, and can climb like a demon up those trails. I used to hike all the time when I was in school, almost every weekend and occasionally even when I had classes to attend during the week. Academics have never been my strong suit, but the feel of that dry breeze as you summit one of the Valley's mountains is just wildly exhilarating. I even rode my bike around Granite Mountain a few times, till I wiped out and spectacularly tore up my left side.

Tom's Thumb is a lot more difficult than it looks. Just the walk from the parking lot to the trailhead is all uphill and fairly steep. Before you even start the switchbacks, you're pretty winded. And those switchbacks are nothing to sneeze at. Tom's Thumb may not be a sexy climb like Camelback Mountain, but it's a full-throttle hike for an amateur. Once you get past the crazy steep switchbacks, about a mile or so in, the hike teases you with a relatively long flat stretch. There, you can catch your breath, try to persuade your tiny, athletic girlfriend to slow down, and gird your loins for the final boulder-scramble at the end. Finally, after clambering over boulders the size of Buicks, you reach the apex of the hike, a hollow at the base of an enormous house-sized boulder, the eponymous "thumb." I'm sure it's exhilarating – it was for Molly – but I was so exhausted at the top that it was all I could do to nod at her and fumble for my water bottle. And I like to pretend I'm in decent shape. For a skinny guy.

"This is going to be our spot," Molly pronounced. "Our special place."

"Couldn't you find someplace a little, um, flatter?" I gasped.

She grinned. "Gives you something to work up to, doesn't it?"

Molly was right. We hiked the Thumb many times after that. While it never got "easy," it stopped completely kicking my ass after a few more tries. One time, on a morning particularly free from other hikers, we stopped and reclined on one of the flat expanses beneath the Thumb, panting and sweating, but dizzy with the fun of it. The whole North Valley spread below us, and we could just barely discern some tiny figures at the trailhead below. The sunlight was starting to strengthen and the countryside, which had seemed to be tinted only in grayscale, began to bloom with color.

"Rebirth," said Molly, looking at me with those strange light blue eyes of hers. "Every day is a rebirth, Ben." Then she grinned, rolled closer to me, and pulled down my shorts. It was brief, but mind-flaying. Someone might have noticed us, but by that point I was beyond caring. I lay on the face of that boulder for a long time afterwards, feeling the morning sun burn into my shoulders, while

Molly quietly chewed some almonds and drank water.

Hiking together became an obsession of mine after that point, as one might assume. It became our shared euphemism for outdoor carnality. Molly cultivated my desire expertly, doling out her availability like a trail of breadcrumbs in the forest. I would actually plead with her to hike with me. When we finally left for a climb, I'd be so excited I'd practically sprint to the peak. The landscape of the Valley of the Sun etched a visual record of our trysts; our love became the horizon. The sun literally rose and set on us.

I will never hit the trails here again, of course. Not without her. My legs, which had become crazy-toned from our time together, are skinny again. I need another hobby. I need another life. I need Molly to come back. Molly will never come back. I scared her off. I clung too tightly. I wanted not just to live with her, but to inhale her, sweat her out through my pores. And when Molly (understandably) freaked out at my outrageous clinginess, I accused her of betrayal. I was drunk with love of her, bewitched.

I scared her away.

There has never, in the history of the world, been a bigger asshole than me. Losing the literal best thing that has ever happened to me.

*

"Hey Ben, can you run my drinks over to Table 7?" Zach pleads, snapping me back to the present. "I need to deal with that big party at 3."

I've been daydreaming, but damn, the kid really needs to start getting his shit together if he wants to make it a place like El Mescal. I realize I am thinking like a manager, and not like a musician who does this job only to be able to afford a new amplifier. That's really dangerous territory. I'd better not let that happen again.

"No worries," I say. "Chill." I am reassuring, an elder statesman of sorts. Zach's eyes lose a little of that manic gleam, and I help him limp to the end of our shift relatively unscathed.

Zach asks me if I want to get a drink as we leave El Mescal. It actually feels really good that Zach is doing this purely out of gratitude for my helping him out tonight. Trust me, I've had far too many people buy me sympathy drinks since Molly left. I cannot deal with another pity beer. Gratitude, though, I can handle, so we walk down the block to Saddlebags, a dumpy little honky-tonk wannabe that bears the singular distinction of the coldest draft beers in the East Valley. Because it's on the corner of Fifth Avenue, it gets a good nighttime crowd, even though it isn't obviously in-your-face or hipster like El Mescal or Loco Patron or just about every other place in this neighborhood.

"Did you notice Kimberly tonight?" Zach asks. "She was in fine form." Kimberly is one of the bartenders, and I honestly cannot remember a single thing about her that I noticed from tonight, but I nod wisely. It wouldn't do to let down Zach's image of me too immediately.

"Do you think it'd be ok with management if I asked Kimberly out one of these days?" I'm surprised; Zach is practically just out of training and he already wants to make a move on the Mixologist Mistress? Good for him.

"Management couldn't care less," I told him, "but Kim'll eat you for lunch." We laugh and drink.

Zach is from San Diego originally, came to the area to attend ASU, and after five years he is more or less still a student but not quite sure what he wants to do when he grows up. So he waits tables at El Mescal a few shifts a week, with a side gig as a dog-walker. He tells great stories about the dogs. I like hearing them for the names alone; people really name their pets some crazy names.

"There are three Chihuahuas that I walk every day. Chanel, Halston and Valentina. A Dachshund named Basil. And then there's Duke, the Great Pyrenees."

"That's the big fluffy white kind of dog, right?" I ask. As a profoundly dog-allergic person, I've always longed for one.

"Yep. Duke is two and he's huge. He looks like Falcor the Luck Dragon."

"Ha! *Neverending Story.*" We clink our drafts.

Zach may be just another kid with a lot to learn about waiting tables during the weeds, but he is also a bit of a hero. Not long ago, while walking dogs in Eldorado Park, he found an old lady lying in the sidewalk who'd fallen and couldn't get up. Zach called 911 and stayed with her till the ambulance came. Would I have done the same, or would I have mistaken her for one of the many homeless people that hang out around there? There are quite a few homeless in the Phoenix area, which makes perfect sense in the winter, but I can't imagine a more hellish existence than being without proper air-conditioning here in the summer months. This area is fine, if you are equipped for it. Otherwise, it'll broil your brains inside your skull.

"So, do you think you guys will still be playing at like eight on Sunday?" asks Zach. "I've got an afternoon shift that day, but I don't want to miss you."

"Should be fine," I reply. "Hope you can stop by."

When I am not get harassed by bachelorettes and crying over my lost love, I play in a band. We've played together for years now. We started out way back when Rory and I were at ASU together, calling ourselves "Horse Divorce." No, I'm not proud of the name. But back then, in our beer and weed-infused fog, we thought that a play on words for the pronunciation of *hors d'oeuvres* was perhaps the funniest name for a college band ever.

Despite our moronic nomenclature, Rory and I found that his bass and my guitar put together some great sound. We grabbed the always affable Kyle Hanson for drums, and there we were. The perfect college sound: classic covers of Bob Seger, Counting Crows, Coldplay, and then the obligatory Gin Blossoms numbers. (Since the Gin Blossoms are from Tempe, literally every local cover band is obligated to finish at least one set with "Hey Jealousy.") After one lucky shot playing an out-of-the-way corner during the Tempe Marketplace Street Fair our junior year, we got noticed. Suddenly it was Horse Divorce, playing at the Phi Tau party. Horse Divorce, doing an acoustic set at the coffee house on Apache or at Casey Moore's Oyster House.

Of course, it was all that play-time that sort of contributed to my taking a leave of absence from ASU and my erstwhile attempt at a Sociology major. Not that it was really going anyplace as it was. I rationalized this change in study plans to my parents by explaining that at least Horse Divorce helped pay rent, unlike my previous job of racking up a string of embarrassing C's in Human Behavior.

81

They agreed to not murder me, as long as I took at least some part-time classes in something practical, like Real Estate. I think they figured it was temporary, some under-the-skin itch I needed to resolve before I grew up and started wearing Dockers. We were all a little naïve in those days.

I left full-time academia, giving a half-hearted effort at some online coursework, while priming the band's potential for superstardom. What I now have, at 27 years old, is a recurring gig at the Yucca Taproom and some shifts serving drinks at El Mescal. And the sweet memory of the months I co-habitated with most beautiful girl in the Valley of the Sun, of course. Don't forget that claim to fame.

Rory and I came to our senses after a while, and got rid of our first stupid name in favor of a second, equally stupid, name. We started calling ourselves *Difficult Citrus*, which was at least kind of funny. At least with a name like Difficult Citrus, nobody asked us, in concerned tones, whether someone in the band had suffered through a bad relationship. With Difficult Citrus, we were merely another dumb-ass band that played decent music.

The big difference – that emerged from our supposed "seriousness" in the new name – was that we started writing our own music. Well, *I* started writing all our music. We didn't get the frat party gigs anymore, but rather the more subdued venues, where the floors weren't sticky with beer and brawls didn't break out in the crowd while we played. Our audiences were practically highbrow in comparison. We rose to the occasion. It was Rory who suggested we pick a classier-sounding name, something to showcase our newly-gained respectability. We became The Ben Gibley Trio. Which paid the rent at a *better* class of shithole apartment off Broadway Road in Tempe.

I bid Zach a good night, and find my way back to my car. On my way down Hayden, I see that Carlsbad Tavern is still going strong, despite it being well after one. Carlsbad is the only place I know of in this area that stays open till 2:30 am. Subsequently, it's where most of the servers go to drink after they get off work in this corner of town. Many a pity beer was purchased for me at Carlsbad recently. I'm keeping well away from that joint; anyway, I'm tired. Not that this would be late for

Phoenix or Tempe, but Scottsdale has a different vibe; I guess money needs to sleep. It's mostly because it's an older population in this area. Now that they've been building more condos and apartment complexes, a younger crowd is moving in, but things take a while to change. Onto the mostly empty Pima Freeway, South to Tempe.

Tempe doesn't have the signage and zoning restrictions that they have in Scottsdale, so there's neon and billboards and graffiti (*public art*, says Molly's voice) and a lot more garbage here. Tempe is where the people who run all the over-priced Scottsdale boutiques and wellness spas live. And those who sling out the tequila shots too, I guess. Home, sweet home is Fiesta Village apartments, which makes up for its shabbiness by its proximity to Mekong Market and all the best pan-Asian food in the entire state. From Korean to Vietnamese, this neighborhood has everything. Fiesta Village is not a high-rise like many Tempe apartments that cater to the perpetually semi-broke student milieu; just four floors. I'm on the third floor, which can get freaky hot in the summer, but it's got a balcony overlooking the anemic little "courtyard" where one can relax and smoke when one doesn't want one's entire apartment to smell like weed.

Juno is right there to greet me, yowling angrily that I left her alone so long. Her claws dig into my thighs; yeah, she's definitely mad that I had a late shift. Since Molly packed up all her funky textiles and left me weeping on the loveseat, Juno's been very affectionate with me, curling up in my lap and purring like a freight train. Cats can be very sensitive to emotions, not that my emotions haven't been out there for all to see. Rory tells me I wear my sadness like a superhero wears a cape. Which, if it weren't so disparaging of me, I think would make pretty cool lyrics to put into a song.

There's an accusatory pile of dirty laundry in the corner of my bedroom. I am in no mood to wash clothes, and what's the point anyway? I have enough boxer briefs to last me for the next couple days. I don't go back to El Mescal for a couple days, so I don't have to worry about dress shirts. I am wholly aware that I'm living like a college student, despite being almost thirty.

When I finally fall asleep, I have an insanely vivid dream about that time that Molly and I went to that fucked up old amusement park. It has been awhile since I last dreamed of her. When Molly first left me, I had dreams (visions?) of her pretty much every night. Some of them were so realistic-seeming that I'd wake up expecting to see Molly lying there beside me, her eyes all squinty with sleep, her hair messy.

*

The amusement park, Castles and Coasters was its weird name, has been around since the Seventies, a weird place that grew out of being a mini golf course. The rides just sort of mushroomed around the park haphazardly over the years. It was the kind of place that tries to be charming and settles for being semi-creepy and quirky. But it was the perfect place for Molly and me. It was one of her favorite spots.

They had a pirate theme and a jungle theme and a Wild West theme going simultaneously, which, instead of making the park feel schizophrenic, gave us the impression of a benign form of chaos. No matter where you stood, you could hear Steve Winwood and Jimmy Buffett music playing through tinny speakers. Clearly not caring too much about trademark infringement, the park had a Pirate statue made to look almost exactly like Johnny Depp playing Jack Sparrow. We called him Jim Bluebird.

"Take me on the carousel!" Molly cried. "I want to ride the goat."

Along with the mundane horses, this carousel also offered rides on rabbits, goats, and ostriches. The jangly calliope music was merely piped in, and we were surrounded by little kids, but it was glorious.

"You know, goats are often viewed as Familiars," Molly told me. "Spirit animals for witches."

"It's their eyes," I said. "Look how creepy. Those sideways pupils."

"They're beautiful," Molly protested and stroked her goat's long, twisted horns.

I rode a horse, white with blue ribbons in her mane, her mouth opened in a silent scream of despair that she was stuck on this rickety carousel in a strange park just off the highway to downtown Phoenix.

We bought cherry slushies and sat at a picnic table instead, watching the faces of screaming teens as Desert Storm, the signature thrill coaster, completed its loops. We rode the Sky-diver, a free fall drop tower. The anticipation was so much worse than the actual, anticlimactic fall. We slowly rose, watching the palm trees row smaller beneath our feet, and then we were far beyond the tops of the palms and could see out west towards downtown.

The city of Phoenix really does not have the greatest skyline, and it's pretty shitty up close, but the mountains in the distance looked gorgeous as ever. I'm a total baby about heights and I wanted to die right there, but I couldn't let on to Molly that I was a coward. I wanted to pretend to some Gallant Masculine Chivalry and hold her hand reassuringly, but with the neck harness on, I couldn't reach her. So much for faux gallantry. Our feet dangled, vulnerable and useless. Then we dropped and I screamed like a girl and Molly practically peed herself laughing at me.

Splash Down, the flume ride. Banging up against the side of the fiberglass chute. The hollow fiberglass log passed a tiny Wild West town, complete with diminutive shops: *Goldie's Saloon, Boots-N-Stuff,* and (Molly's favorite) *The Pickle Place* – whose sign was a sentient pickle wearing a Stetson because well this was the Wild West. Or was it? The mural on the wall nearby depicted a lion devouring a zebra, as well as loin-cloth wearing native bearing spears, inexplicably accompanied by Fred Flintstone. Truly.

"Whoever painted these dropped some major acid," I quipped.

Molly laughed and leaned back against me as the log clattered away. We bumped roughly through a tunnel, the walls of which were dotted with constellations of chewing gum, ostensibly placed there by brave prior passengers of Splash Down.

"Why? Just why?" She laughed.

"I think, years ago maybe one guy put his gum there as a joke. And then someone saw it and thought it was funny and he puts his gum there. And after that, it became a thing." I guessed. "Maybe local kids bring packs and packs of gum, just to see if they can get it on the walls of this shitty little tunnel. Maybe if they make it, they have bragging rights for the night. Got my gum on the wall!"

"Oh, Ben, you're over-thinking it, but I love you," said Molly, and my heart sang.

We passed a small lagoon, where there was a shipwrecked raft, bearing a skeleton, its bony arm outreached. "Dead men tell no tales," Molly intoned. The ride attendants, who looked like they still required babysitting, were dressed like that meth-head kid from *Breaking Bad.* The sound system was so jacked up that you couldn't hear them giving instructions on safety; we had to rely on hand gestures and common sense for where to enter and exit the ride.

The sun set behind the mountains, and the park blossomed into a neon and colored-light magic show. All the dusty creepiness of the afternoon was made magical. Even the funnel cakes smelled better. We rode the "magic carpet" (basically a ride on a circular, dipping track that went backwards halfway through) and the air was filled with red and green and gold neon lights, and the sounds of cheesy eighties music and the Girl (*woman*!!) of My Dreams was at my side, laughing and screaming in pretend fear as we swept around the track. I didn't want the night to end, so we went to the arcade and played air hockey and Whack-A-Mole. At the Claw Machine, I actually hooked a stuffed pink rabbit.

Now, everybody knows that Claw Machines are totally rigged, and one or two people per *century* actually hook a toy. So this rabbit was a huge deal to me, and of course, of symbolic importance regarding Molly and me. The rabbit became *my* familiar. I bring him (yes, he's a boy) with me to work at El Mescal and put him in my apron pocket, so that his little ears and nose are poking out. He is my totem, one of the few tangible reminders of my time with Molly.

"I like your little friend," some bachelorette party-goer will say. "Does he have a name?"

"Jack Rabbit." I reply, which make the customers laugh, and if that translates to better tips, then it's fine by me.

I wrote a pretty good song called "Jackrabbit Dreams," which has become very popular in our small but growing circulation. The crowd at the

Yucca Taproom loves it, so we always end our sets with it. It's a perfect finale song: upbeat, hopeful against all odds. But enough about me, ha ha. When Rory hits the opening chords for "Jackrabbit Dreams," I pull that little bunny out of my pocket and hold him up to the microphone as I sing. It's cheesy, sure, but I've gotten used to doing it, and by now, it's practically a good luck charm for the Trio. Believe it or not, some of the girls (*women!*) in the audience even know the lyrics.

> *I found your hair tie*
> *Under my bed*
> *And made believe you were still here*
> *I saw the sun rise over Granite Mountain*
> *Pretending you were at my side*
> *How could I let you slip away?*
> *How could I have hurt you?*
> *My sweet woman*
> *My lovely lady*
> *I only see you in my dreams*

There are other songs about Molly, ones that I wrote when we were happily a couple. For example, we almost always begin our sets with "Sunshine Face," about the way she used to look in the morning. Molly is not a morning person. Even when we'd get up to go on hikes, she needed to stop and get cans of energy drinks to get herself motivated to move. For someone so into natural fibers, vegetarianism, and purity, Molly loved those gross caffeine bombs in a can.

*

In my dream, we are riding in those crazy go-karts, looping around and around, but my kart won't go. I'm stuck in the middle of the track while Molly and the other riders zip past me. I'm calling out for the ride attendants to help me out, but as often happens in dreams, I have no voice. So I sit there, trying to move, motionless. Gee, I wonder how to interpret this? Why am I so blatantly obvious in my sleep; can't I dream symbolically like everyone else in the world?

*

My phone buzzes. By the light filtering in, it must be late morning already. It's Jimmy, so I pick up. Jimmy manages the Yucca Taproom, where we play every Thursday night and most Sundays. The Ben Gibley Trio even has a little bit of a following there. They like our real music, not just our early 2000s covers and golden oldie 80s specials. Jimmy is a good guy; he sprays us all over his social media and lets us take our time setting up. Yucca gets a cool crowd of music nerds, rockers, and the types who go there to drink micro-brews with stupid names like Dead Armadillo Lager and Rattlesnake Milk IPA. But the bottom line is we've gotten great play-time. Sure, I make more money doling out shots to bridesmaids at El Mescal on Friday nights, but it's a sweet deal to play our music.

"What's up?" I ask.

"Hey, Benjy," he drawls. "You up for a last minute gig? Like real last minute. Tonight."

"I'll have to check with Rory and Kyle, but I don't know if --"

"Rory'll drop whatever co-ed he's into for this show." Jimmy cuts me off. "Camp Verde Lounge. You get to open for the headline act. Ava Hernandez.

You heard of her? She's huge with the teenagers, started on Vine, then moved to TikTok. Anyway, the vocalist in her regular opening act tested positive for Covid; she needs a substitute act -- pronto. Place'll be filled with teeny-boppers from Chandler and Scottsdale."

I tell Jimmy yes before even texting the guys. He's right; they'll drop what they're doing for this one. It's a gift from the Music Gods. I almost start a text message to Molly. Jesus, stop it, Ben. What are you thinking? Whether it's because I want to think she'd be happy for me, or rather to let her know that I am not a complete mess without her, I'm not sure. But there's really not time for that anyway. I've got to find Rory.

*

There was this time, I think it was our sophomore year at ASU together. At any rate, it was before Horse Divorce got any real playing time. Rory and I sat in his apartment, drinking beer and listening to music, talking about what bullshit our classes were. We spent hours talking about what we would do when we made it big.

"I'm going to buy a Gretsch Ranch Falcon, like Jack White plays," Rory claimed. "He makes it sound just like a bass. So sweet!"

"No way, man," I drawled. "That's shit. I'm getting a Sunburst 1956 Brownie Fender Stratocaster."

"Like Clapton!"

"Just like fuckin' Clapton!"

We went on to discuss the girls (definitely not *ladies*, this time, sorry, Molly) who would someday scream for us and throw their panties at the stage when we played. We named all sorts of vile, fantastical acts these females would perform for us, just for the privilege of being near the Coolest New Band of the 21st Century. And how we'd concoct elaborate contractual riders for our concerts, and make the staff serve us.

"They'll have to fly in the Pollo Asado burritos from Illegal Pete's." I said. "Those things are the bomb. And give us bowls of Hot Cheetos."

"And Dom!" Rory laughed. "Bottles of Dom."

Neither of us had ever tried Dom Perignon; I'm not sure we'd ever had any kind of champagne at that point. The name just evoked stardom, which would be ours for the taking in just a few months.

Jesus, we were young then. What a couple of goofballs. Jesus, Rory has always been there for me and I never even realized it. I love that guy.

*

My phone buzzes and there is Rory, in fine form. He's gotten my urgent text message.

"Holy shit, dude!" he cries. "That Hernandez kid is huge! I mean, not huge-huge, but freaking *crazy* huge compared to anyone else we've ever played with! She'll have hundreds of fans there, and they'll all have their cameras and they'll put it out on Instagram. This is fucking amazing!"

"Maybe shave before tonight," I tell him. "Those teenagers want to see sweet-faced guys, not bums like you. You don't want to scare anyone off before we can get discovered."

"Hello, Pot." returns Rory. "My name is Kettle. Before you get all uppity on my facial hair, you might want to check in on that long term melancholy you've had going for the past two months. Snap the fuck out of it for tonight, ok? You can do what you want tomorrow."

"I get it, Rore," I say. "I hear you loud and clear."

"Alright, then. Make yourself nice and pretty, but not too pretty. What time do they want us over there? I need to find someone who can move our amps."

I hang up with Rory, and go through an almost identical conversation with Kyle. Except for the snapping out of it stuff; Kyle doesn't push at me the way Rory does. He's very circumspect.

"Everything happens for a reason, Benny." Kyle intones somberly.

When I am packing up my guitars, I realize that the little stuffed rabbit is not in his usual spot on my nightstand.

I panic.

I empty all the dresser drawers, throwing all my boxers and tee shirts on the floor in a frantic search for Jack Rabbit. I throw discarded towels around like a crazy man. Juno leaps atop my bed and glares at me. I remember having the rabbit in my apron pocket at El Mescal last night. One of the drunk girls in the *I Do Crew* tried to grab him, and I had to do a quick hip swivel to keep her away. It's going to be alright; my heart slows down a bit. He's almost certainly in the restaurant; I just won't have time to drive all the way into Old Town to retrieve him today. It's going to be fine.

I sit down on the bed and Juno hops into my lap. Her purring settles me down a little. She's right. Calm down, Ben, for God's sake. Be happy. Think about tonight. Think about the opportunity. You've been waiting for this for years; don't fuck it up now after all this time. I take a few deep breaths and pet Juno. Her claws dig into my thighs.

Out of nowhere, I decide to text my dad and fill him in about the show. He responds almost immediately, and his congratulatory all-caps message is a happy surprise. He tells me that he and Mom will be there. They want to be able to say they were around when their kid made it big. He says Mom just told Lynn, who is calling all her friends in the Phoenix area. Everyone is just crazy-excited about this, he says.

I'm proud of you, he says.

One final quick sweep under the bed. No stuffed bunny in sight, but there's an impressive amount of *dust* bunnies. See? I'm fine. I'm perfectly fine. I can even make jokes about this. I find some relatively-unscathed jeans. After a brief search, the only clean tee shirt I can find is from that sad little amateur theater where Molly sometimes volunteered. Costuming, of course. She used to tell the most hilarious stories about that crew. Well, it'll have to do. At least it's local, which is always good. And a non-profit. That's not a bad image to project when you're the *Local Act Opening for Ava Hernandez*, right? I think that it's a decent look for me tonight. I think, wherever she is, Molly might even like it.

THE DRIVE UP FROM TUCSON

I don't think I will ever forget how happy I was that New Year's Eve. We were at the Gala at Ventana Canyon Club. Everything was lovely. Jeff, Sadie, and I had just gotten back from a long weekend in Breckenridge that we snuck in right after Christmas. Jeff didn't even complain about the exorbitant ticket price for the Gala because he'd made such a killing in the market all year.

We sat with Marci and Jim Villette, of course. Marci and I had spent close to three hours earlier in the day getting Blood Orange Body Scrub Massages at the Hacienda Del Sol Spa, and then getting blow-outs and make-up at Bombshell 7. I hadn't felt that glamorous since well before Sadie was born. My dress was a copper-colored silk sheath, my finger- and toenails were lacquered a lovely shade of bordeaux. I wore the silver necklace Jeff had gotten me for our fifteenth wedding anniversary last year, the one he bought for me during our trip to Venice. Marci sparkled in a curve-hugging beaded black dress. Our men were in their regulation holiday tuxedos with tartan bowties. We felt like – and, dare I say it, *looked* like – celebrities out on the town.

We'd been drinking even before we drove out to Ventana Canyon. Sadie was safely stowed away at Caroline's for a sleepover (God Bless Caroline's mother, Elsie, and her infinite patience with sullen teens!). The orchestra at Ventana Canyon played mellow jazz standards that even Jeff consented to dance to. The steak and lobster dinner was predictably magnificent, the conversation effervescent. Marci and I never stopped laughing. At midnight, Jeff and I necked like a couple kids. It was a perfectly grand evening.

People tend to consider Tucson to be Phoenix's poor relation, its shabby cousin to the South, and sure, we're is much smaller and less glamorous. But Tucson can still put on one helluva good party. Particularly in the Golf Club scene. And New Year's Eve at Ventana Canyon was such a party.

I remember how Jeff got our keys from the valet when we headed home, sometime after one-thirty, I think. It was cold, and I had Jeff's tuxedo jacket over my shoulders like a girl with her prom date. As we drove back home, down the sloping highway of the Catalina Foothills, you could see Christmas lights everywhere throughout, like a giant had thrown a cache of jewels down the mountainside. There was snow on Mount Lemmon. I felt beautiful and fulfilled and giddy. It was like some magnificent dream. I thought to myself, well, it doesn't get much better than this. This is it.

We are by no means in the stratosphere. I'm just a Tucson housewife, though the wife of an Engineer. I'm spoiled, but not pampered. I'm practical; I drive an Acura, not a Range Rover. Nothing particularly fabulous ever happens to me, but then again, nothing terrible ever happens either. Jeff goes to work, Sadie goes to school; I go to yoga. We have a lovely house on the base of Coronado Mountain, on Calle Bendita, in fact. From our poolside patio, you get a nice view of downtown Tucson.

Jeff works too much and is far too serious all the time. He is not the most affectionate perhaps; his work stresses him out, and he is not the type to complain aloud. But he is a wonderful father.

Our daughter, Sadie, is a work in progress, spirited and blessed with a healthy dose of sarcasm. We butt heads; I won't sugarcoat that one. Sadie is fourteen and often inscrutable. But she is my pride and joy, and sometimes even Sadie recognizes it.

I have a terrific bunch of girlfriends, starting with Marci. We share everything, laughing more than we talk. Like a sorority without any monthly dues. We meet at the park behind Sunrise Elementary School every morning with our dogs and walk up the winding roads up Shadow Ridge. We volunteer together at Friends of Sabina Canyon and the Empire Ranch Foundation. We've driven each other home when one of us got over-served. We've helped each other pick out paint colors for our various homes' rehab projects. We orchestrate our kids' activities together: ballet, soccer, the usual drill. We keep each other sane. I would trust these ladies with my life.

The days are almost always sunny and the nights are cool. The biggest worry on the horizon is whether Sadie will stop wearing only hoodies and leggings to school. Or whether I'll have time to get a new dress for the Casa De Los Ninos Fundraiser that's looming on the horizon. And if I don't get a new dress, will I still fit in that pretty of-the-shoulder navy blue gown I've got? I'm clearing the table after we enjoyed some grilled tilapia when it happens. A four word text from Mom up in Scottsdale.

Broke hip, in hospital.

And just like that, the gentle trajectory of my life takes a turn and now I am living a hundred plus miles away from my home, out at my widowed mother's place while she awaits hip surgery. Jeff has sprung to attention, ready to attend to Sadie's various chauffeuring needs in my absence. Marci, who is the absolute best, has offered to bring meals over and walk our Golden Retriever, Rosie. As of now, everyone in my little circle is getting along fine and moving on with their lives, while I am here and nothing changes.

The days are simplified into repeating patterns. Watch the hospital staff patrol the hallways, then come in to check her vitals, fill her pitcher. Acknowledge the cheerful nurses as they change shifts around 7:00 pm. The night nurses are always a little more subdued than the unnaturally-caffeinated day nurses. The constant patter: *sweetheart, honey, doll, lovey.* I know they mean well, but it offends me, this familiar banter of theirs.

They consult a chart. "Oh, so you had a fall, is that it?" they ask my mother. And then I tell them the story, or I listen to Mom tell it. When I get to tell the story, I say: "She fell down in the park and broke her hip." Mom's version is a little more elaborate. She begins: "Well, my husband died about five months ago…" Dissolve into the next day and it's the same.

The nurses here all look the same. They are uniformly big, round-shouldered girls with dark blond hair and high-pitched voices. Pouchy bellies, straining against their scrubs. Are they physically bigger nurses because this is the orthopedics floor, I wonder? We keep the door to my mother's room open, and watch the nurses as they walk patients down the hallway in their grippy socks. Walking like that is a crazy pipe-dream for us. Mom's left leg is turned out so far that her pinkie toe rests on the bed. She's not going anywhere.

I tell the passage of time by medication distributions. "Oh, I'll bring your medication right on in." they sing. I have my favorite nurses and also those I cannot stand. For example, Lupe is good, though she repeats herself, asking the same things over and over. "Oh, so you're on a cardiac diet, is that right?" And Rosalyn (spelled that way, but pronounced "Rosa-Lynn," which she never fails to remind us) is crazy annoying. Rosalyn is an older nurse, maybe in her fifties. She is sharp-nosed, with a tight, dark ponytail. And a cackle. Oh, dear lord, what a cackle. After every phrase, she lets it loose: a signature *heh heh heh*! "I know you like your ice water, Dolores, *heh heh heh*!" "You're watching Wheel of Fortune again, Dolores? *heh heh heh*!"

Mom hates her too, which is comforting.

I get to the hospital at eight, the earliest I am allowed in. We watch *Good Morning America* from eight am till noon. And then more news. The television is never off, but babbles on incessantly.

She had a fall. Mom. While walking her new puppy at a park in Scottsdale. She's not super clear on how it all came down, but the long and the short of it is that her femur has been broken in three places. When I first read that four word text message from Mom, I just sort of stood there stupidly, trying to come to terms with what it said. I was preparing to call Mom back and ask if she was joking when I got an incoming call from Shea Medical Center. "Is this Loretta Kremer? I'm afraid your mother has been admitted here." The next thing I knew, I was driving up I-17 behind all the big semis, sniffling back tears rushing to see my poor eighty year-old mother who was lying helpless in the hospital because her idiot dog tripped her.

The funny thing is, we'd actually had plans to meet up the next day. Mom was planning on coming down to see the Tucson Symphony Orchestra with me. The Music of John Williams. I don't generally like going to the symphony, but this was music I knew. We'd made reservations for lunch at Pho Thu, the nearby Vietnamese place. Mom was going to slip Sadie some extra cash too, she'd told me conspiratorially. We were going to make quite a nice little afternoon of it.

When I first find Mom in the Emergency Room (they still hadn't transferred her to a real room yet – after four hours! -- because of something about beds not being available, which was rather astounding) the first thing she says is: "I'm so sorry you're going to miss the show!" Then she asks about her new puppy and bursts into tears.

That first night, Mom is kept in a quiet-ish corner of the ER, in a little room with a sliding plexiglass door that keeps most of the noise out. The less lucky folks are laid up in gurneys lining the hallway. I see them every time I leave Mom's side to use the

Ladies Room. Some people are holding up bandaged arms, some slump over in a heap. A few are children, being comforted by their parents and their iPads. I count my blessings that Mom at least gets a nook of her own.

Ultimately, we have to wait almost twenty-four hours before a bed opens up on the Orthopedics floor. Mom won't eat the food they bring her, so I drive out to Jack in the Box and got us both some Jumbo Jack burgers. They taste awful, but cannot possibly be as bad as that hospital food looks. The fries are cold.

In her fancy new room in Orthopedics up on the sixth floor, nurses come in every hour or two to see Mom. Compared to our solitary time in the ER, this activity feels almost intrusive. They check her vitals and ask her about pain. They are especially interested in my mother's medications. Mom's got a heart condition, Atrial Fibrillation, among several other less intimidating ailments. Because of this, she takes a blood thinner. This is a problem. The surgeon can't operate on Mom's hip for at least five days. Until the Xarelto gets out of her system.

"So I just have to lie here and wait?" Mom starts sniffling again. The orthopedic surgeon, a surprisingly paunchy, bald fellow with a drawl, has finally come to see her. The man has a limp so pronounced it's more of a lurch.

"Well, ma'am, it's generally preferable to wait, instead of you having a stroke while we operate." the affable physician retorts. He clearly fancies himself a comedian; as he paces her room, he waggishly pulls on Mom's big toe (her right foot, on the unbroken leg). This action proves that my mother must truly be under the influence of morphine; she had never in my lifetime let anyone touch her feet.

"Maybe we shouldn't operate after all," says Mr. Funnyman Surgeon. "But then again, you know what they do to horses when they break a leg, right? Haha."

"Yeah, haha," says Mom dryly. She may be shot full of narcotics, but I can tell she doesn't like this guy.

"I'll see you in a few days. Don't run away now."

The surgeon limps slowly out of her room and into the bowels of the hospital. This is all an elaborate joke at my expense; surely someone will jump out from being the curtains and tell me I've won a prize for being so gullible as to believe this wacky scenario of my mother with the broken femur and the limping orthopedic surgeon who pulls her toes and makes jokes about shooting her. Nothing is real anymore. The constant tight knot in the pit of my stomach is the only thing I can feel. Visiting hours are over for the day. Five more days till surgery can go forward.

We have to make some sort of decision about the dog, Walter. That's one of the most pressing issue, since we are in a holding pattern about surgery. At least we are not forced to confront any further reality, like what the future holds for Mom now. We can wrap our brains around the issue of what to do with the dog. If Jeff and Sadie and I lived nearer, we could maybe take care of him for her. But we're over a hundred miles away.

The problem is, Mom got the puppy because she was lonely after Dad died last year. Being alone after sixty years was awful for her. Getting a dog didn't seem too crazy of an idea. Mom was a fit, active person, always gardening and doing "power walks" on 96th Street adjacent to her subdivision. She didn't want a rescue dog, *didn't want to inherit someone else's problems*, she'd said. Mom was so excited when she found a Basset Hound breeder out near Globe. We drove out there together, to Ascher's Hounds, and picked out the sweetest-looking puppy in a litter of five. A tri-color pup, full of piss and vinegar, as they used to say.

"His name is Walter." Mom said, as the pup gnawed on her fingers. "Hello, Wally!"

It was mutual love at first sight. Mom kept telling us how the little guy "saved her life." That is, of course, until the little guy broke her hip. Fucking Wally.

My daughter, Sadie, called it. She was the only skeptical one. "Bad idea," she'd intoned ominously when I told her of her grandmother's desire to get a puppy. "This will not end well." She called me an "enabler" for assisting Mom in her purchase.

Potty-training had been abysmal, Mom reported. A stubborn Basset, paired with an elderly lady with no desire to be a disciplinarian during her Golden Years, is a terrible combination. Wally piddled everywhere. Then he'd scratch at the back door to go out back, sniff all the bushes and rocks, lifting his stubby little legs dutifully. Upon re-entering Mom's house, Wally would scamper about, then blithely crap on the bedroom carpet. Mom didn't care.

"I have plenty of time to teach him," she'd said.

Wally became used to camping out between Mom's legs, lovingly staring up at her with big melted chocolate eyes. He cried, and she brought him treats. Wally liked getting his way, and Mom liked having someone to indulge. It was a match made in heaven.

And then one sunny afternoon, when Mom took little Wally for a walk in Eldorado Park, he wrapped the leash around her legs, and the rest is history.

"Take care of my little buddy," Mom says weeping.

"Of course, Mom. I'll take care of everything," I reply.

"Oh, Wally," cries Mom. "My sweet little puppy. I love him so."

"I know, Mom." I start flipping through the channels to see if *Jeopardy!* is on yet. She loves *Jeopardy!*

It ends up that when your dog trips you up and breaks your hip when you're all alone in a public park, the EMT people call the local Animal Shelter to take him in. I make a couple calls, then drive out to Lucky Paws Animal Shelter on Thomas.

For almost killing my mother, Wally looks pretty innocent, though it's hard to look too menacing when you're a Basset Hound puppy. The little bugger wags his tail so hard that his entire rump vibrates. He steps on own his ridiculous long ears and looks so guilty I can't help snuggling him a little. It's not his fault he's an idiot, after all.

"Come here, beastie," I say and take him back to my mom's small, neat little house on Poinsettia Drive. I have to find someplace to board him; I can't keep coming back here to let him out when I have to be making sure Mom is doing ok at the hospital. Wally hits the tile floor and slides around comically.

Then he piddles next to the fireplace before I have a chance to open up the sliding door to the patio.

I call Jeff and give him the update ("I'll keep you posted") and get ready for bed. The house feels hollow. It was strange enough without my father in it, but now without either of my parents, it is a different entity. No longer inviting and festive.

I turn on the Channel 15 News and make some microwave popcorn. The Cactus League continues its play. Weather is perfect, as usual. There are loads of Farmers Markets popping up in various locations throughout the Valley this weekend. Preparations continue for the Parada Del Sol Rodeo in Scottsdale, tickets now 100% digital!

Wally won't stay in his little doggy bed. Instead, he sits down on the floor, next to the head of the bed and start whimpering until I pick him up and plop him down next to me.

"Don't get used to this, Mister." I warn him. He falls asleep almost immediately. From the amount of dog hair on the comforter, I suspect that Wally hasn't spend many nights in the doggy bed prior to my arrival.

Ultimately, Wally goes to Foothills Animal Rescue, the branch that's off Pima Road, at Mom's insistence. She is convinced that all the wealthy families moving into North Scottsdale will provide her sweet baby the best possible home. I don't tell her that *anyone* can drive up to the shelter; maybe even someone from (gasp!) Flagstaff. She's had enough trauma, with losing little Wally and the possibility of ever walking unassisted or living on her own again all in one week.

The Foothills people are very kind-hearted, and assure me that Wally will be "scooped up" by some lucky new owners right away. A six month old pure bred Basset Hound has got to be a bit of a switch for this place; from what I can see, their adoptable dogs are either Pit Bulls or Chihuahuas.

I tear up saying goodbye to Wally, who waddles away from me without a backward glance. Thanks, little guy. I check Foothills website: twenty-four hours later, Walter has a new home. Damn, that was quick.

Surgery, finally! The would-be comedian orthopedic surgeon with the pot belly puts an eight inch rod into my mother's leg, then adds screws to keep the femur held together. There are two long incisions along her leg, held together with staples. The leg is taut and swollen and angry-looking. Mom is out of it on drugs, but relieved. I report back home to Jeff and Sadie that the procedure was a terrific success. Now Mom will be onto her all-important recovery, which is spent not at the hospital but at a specialized rehabilitation center. Trained professionals will be on staff to help Mom get back on her feet.

After almost a week of being in a holding pattern here at Shea Medical Center, the staff now springs to life. "Have you picked out a facility?" they ask on repeat. I have absolutely no idea how to choose between the different rehab centers, other than proximity to Mom's house and whether Medicare gives them a decent rating. I pick Agave Springs Rehabilitation Center and Long Term Care on Osborne, less than fifteen minutes away from Mom's house. It's effectively a nursing home that has one wing devoted to rehab patients. Mom will be there at least two weeks, they tell me. Probably closer to four.

"I want to go home now," Mom whimpers.

"Dolores, you know you need to learn how to walk again, *heh heh heh.*" says Rosalyn.

Superior Ambulance sends a team of three cheerful women to take Mom to her new home at Agave Springs. Their names are Lindsay, Stacey, and Danielle. Danielle looks younger than my Sadie. Stacey, truth be told, looks a little like the comedienne Melissa McCarthy, red-faced and sarcastic. She crosses her arms over her belly and complains about the heat in Mom's room. And Lindsay, who must be six feet tall, with short cropped hair and a face that radiates capability.

We arrive at Agave Springs much later than expected, after 8:00 pm. "Sorry about that, ma'am," says Stacey, "We had a collision on Highway 60. Lots of casualties." I'm not sure if she's messing with me or not.

This place. I am not prepared for the look of this place. There are shapes slouched in doorways, slumped in wheelchairs, bare backs exposed through hospital gowns. Disheveled white hair. It is a frail, all-white clientele being ministered to by a staff of color.

The word "rehab" sounds so dynamic. My mental image of some gleaming space, vibrating with energy and the desire to overcome adversity screeches to a halt. Agave Springs is evidently a series of long hallways, linked by nursing stations. There appears to be no end in sight.

The Team wheels Mom through the labyrinth in a gurney; they are familiar with this place and greet the staff. They check all the safety features of her new residence, and make sure that all the right procedures were being made for patient transfer.

"This bed doesn't function properly. I am not leaving a patient in a broken bed."

We move Mom to another room. It is shabby and faded, but serviceable, looking more like a Motel Six room than a hospital. The bed protests loudly when its gears are used. I don't want the Superior Ambulance trio to go. They are so odd and yet so capable that I'm fascinated by them.

Pearlie, the head nurse for the Rehab Wing, gives Mom her pain pill. This is important. The Aides cannot distribute narcotics; only nurses can do so. Pearlie writes down the time; pills cannot be administered other than at the rate it says on

Mom's chart. Eight hour doses. The halls smell strongly of urine. There is a call-light for the night nurse constantly beeping outside Mom's bedroom. "Pain!" moans a man's voice. "Pain, nurse!" The staff move slowly. No one is going anywhere; why rush?

We thank Pearlie for Mom's pill. "You welcome," she replies, and shuffles off.

"Rehab" means that for a half hour or forty-five minutes a day, a pair of young women come in and encourage my mother to sit up in bed. That's it. The rest of the day, we do nothing. Our entire existence is geared towards that thirty minutes of effort. Before and after, we wait. It is obscene.

The therapists are uniformly young, energetic women. They are positive and encouraging to Mom. But even with their cheerful efforts, getting Mom to move her leg even an inch or two goes very slowly. It's both pain and the fear of pain for Mom. They are very patient with her, these therapy girls. They rub Mom's shoulders and call her *Dolores*. At least they don't call her *sweetie*. They tell her she looks amazing for her age. They compliment her hair.

Mom is finally able to sit up on the side of the bed, and her face is triumphant. I congratulate her.

Inside I am thinking: my God, it's been six days since surgery and we are excited that she can *sit up*? I think about the Seventies movie, "The Other Side of the Mountain," the one about the skier -- Jill Kinmont --who is paralyzed by a fall. In one melodramatic scene, Jill attempts to demonstrate her motor skills to her boyfriend. The boyfriend hasn't realized (or accepted) the extent of Jill's injuries. After much effort, she finally picks up a potato chip with her hand, exultant. The uncomprehending boyfriend stares at her blankly. "Jill, honey, aren't you going to walk?" he asks. A pivotal moment in the film. She later finds a new boyfriend.

I feel ashamed, and congratulate my mother again.

We watch the morning news programs till around noon, with Mom nodding in and out of sleep. She asks for me the bedpan, I get it for her, and then I empty it in her small bathroom. We talk. We watch home improvement shows and *Law and Order*. She nods off again. She wakes up and asks for another icepack. I try to read a little. I can't concentrate very well. The light in the room is not bright enough, but I don't want to make it brighter, for fear it will wake up Mom.

The food here is pretty awful. She requests soup, and I drive to Panera for some. She eats almost all of it, and nibbles the bread. She says she is full. She wants another pain pill, but cannot request it for twenty more minutes. Time passes, the pill arrives. She sleeps again, her mouth open, breathing deeply.

When I leave Agave Springs after eight, I have notions of going back to Mom's house and drinking heavily. She has beer, and some cans of cocktails, perfect for an afternoon of lounging on her patio or at the pool. I turn on the television as background noise, but the sound of other voices makes me nervous.

I turn off the tv and fall into bed too early. I wake up at four-thirty, and immediately turn the tv on again. I drink Mom's K-cup coffee, after a brief struggle with the Keurig machine. It tastes like dirt to me, but I need the caffeine.

Mom texts me at six, asking me to bring her moisturizer. I am glad that she is thinking of something other than her pain. She texts me that she had a bad night, that she wasn't able to get her pain pill. She says the overnight nurse told her she "wasn't allowed" to get any medication and that now Mom has to wait for the overseeing physician to arrive sometime mid-morning. It's six am. They won't even let me into Agave until eight am.

I try not to let my initial impulse to get into the car take over. I try to outline mentally what I need to do before driving over there. I brush my teeth, pace around the kitchen, walk to the mailboxes down the street to collect her mail. I bring in the newspapers. She gets two papers a day. I pile them on the kitchen table. She will have an impressive reading trove when she returns. Like coming back from a long vacation. Maybe she will enjoy that. The growing pile of newspapers makes my stomach tighten.

When it is seven, I drive to Frye's for a requested muffin and coffee. Mom likes their pistachio muffins. I feel like I may throw up or have to dash for a bathroom. The sidewalks teem with walking couples; bikers already line the streets. You can't really live in this area and not be a morning person, especially at this time of year. I wish they'd stick to the bike paths, though. God knows, there are trails everywhere here. My peripheral vision is constantly glimpsing neon yellow and green shirts. Once I'm onto 90th, the crowds disperse. They are all but vanished by the time I get onto Osborne. It's not a pleasure-biking road. I sign in at the front desk, and walk down the long hallway that smells of urine and scrambled eggs from the breakfast trays. I am perkily cheerful as I open her door.

I am here for moral support. I don't do anything. I retrieve a fallen Kleenex bow. I unwrap cough drops. I hold the Styrofoam cup. I am silent when Mom sleeps, and cheerful when she wakes. I greet every nurse, aide, therapist, and physician as they enter. I am there. I wish I could go back to Mom's place, but when I get back there I don't know what to do.

Cheryl, the wound nurse, waddles in to check my mother's incisions. Cheryl looks like she must weight over three hundred pounds. She uses pliers to take out the staples after a week. The surgical incisions are red; they ooze fluid. Cheryl cleans them without saying a word.

I get back to the house on Poinsettia. There is no sense of relief, of finally being on my own. I watch a little television, shows that I prefer instead of *Law and Order*. Then I fall asleep.

I drive back to Tucson briefly to check in on the family. The world shocks me, its outdoors-ness is jarring. Just getting onto I-17 feels exhilarating, incredible. Normally, I hate this drive. It annoyed me when Jeff first got the job at Raytheon, even though the pay is decent. I used to be a terrible snob about Tucson, preferring the urban bustle of Phoenix, which I believed had more to offer in terms of culture and excitement and dining. But now, heading South through the moonscape of valley in between these two cities, I feel a rush of relief.

I am going home for a little while. Mom may be in limbo and the world has turned upside down, but it won't be forever because Jeff is still at home and Sadie is still at home, and things will become normal once again as long as Mom can ever start to walk again. Right?

I forgot to fill up with gas and now have to pull off the highway at Riggs Road, at that lonely Gulf station. The few people there stare at me. They are all road-weary travelers, denim-clad and suntanned. I must seem ridiculous to them in my cream linen pants. The bathroom is moderately clean, though. It has a sign: "This restroom is for paying customers only. Please be respectful. God Bless You and have a blessed day!"

Back into my Acura. The sun is rising in my face. I play Christmas Carols on Spotify to cheer myself up. Singing along with Bing Crosby and Rosemary Clooney. I never get to do this when Jeff and Sadie are in the car with me. I haven't sung for a long time.

Our choir at St Francis stopped during Covid, of course, and after that I must have gotten preoccupied with something else; it never even occurred to me to get back involved with the choir again. Heathen that I am. The St. Francis Choir was never particularly good, especially with Judy and her crazy vibrato drowning everyone else out. And Dale, our token male participant, sucking up to Father Keith and arguing with our music director, about how *the women were not holding the note long enough in measure twenty; can't you cut them off? They're doing it wrong!*

I don't much miss the choir.

I pass the exit for Florence. What a dumb name for a town. This state has so many evocative and romantic town names: Gila Bend, Tombstone, Strawberry, Snowflake, Carefree. Florence seems awkward in comparison. The witch's hat peak of Mount Picacho comes into view on my right, so I know I'm about forty minutes out.

Our dog, Rosie, is overjoyed to see me, crying and pawing at me. She then settles down immediately and starts whining for treats. Jeff tells me that he doesn't reward her as much as I usually do, and she's getting good habits now that I'm gone most of the time. Thanks, honey. I think about poor dumb little Wally and feel guilty. But Rosie hated Mom's freshly re-homed Basset puppy and would have made his life a living hell. Not to mention mine.

I want to drive around constantly; I want to go into shops. I want to sleep. I want to rediscover Tucson in all its dusty glory. Jeff entertains me with some stories from work. His admins don't know anything; never have. It's been a theme for the ten years he's been at Raytheon. How can this company function? He has nicknames for all his co-workers. One of them he's dubbed "Al Capone." Jeff is under a lot of pressure in his job. I get it. It's actually nice to hear about problems that don't involve anything physical. The stories about forgotten passwords are silly and comforting.

Mom texts me about how her therapy is going. I am so grateful to Jeff that I can be there for Mom. I feel so much better knowing that he's taking care of Sadie, getting her to school, making meals. I leave home and drive back up to Tempe. Mount Picacho's witch hat is on my left side this time.

On the drive back, I talk to Marci on speakerphone. I've missed our morning dog-walks, conversations, lunches, and normalcy. Marci is a godsend; she keeps me up on local gossip. Someone had a birthday party over at the Golf Club, and Brittany Schue got all loaded and started dancing on the tables, Marci tells me, snorting.

"Didn't the staff make her stop?" I ask.

"Oh, yeah, but not until she broke about twenty wine glasses." says Marci. "The kicker is, they charged it to *Donna*. And Donna doesn't want to offend Brittany by asking her to reimburse the Club for the broken glasses because Brittany is the Chair of the Ladies League."

I also missed the big Girls' Weekend up in Sedona. According to Marci, our mutual friend Colleen was "overserved" at Mariposa, and passed out in the Ladies Room; they had to ask the staff to help get her into their Uber ride. The girls all paid top dollar to stay at L'Auberge de Sedona, and in my absence, Marci got stuck rooming with Beth. Which was fine -- until Beth brought out a sound machine to help her sleep. Marci laughs so much telling the story that I laugh too.

"Beth paid all that money to stay at a fancy hotel where there are these lovely sounds of nature right outside her God-damned window, and what does she do? She plays *recorded crickets* on a machine all night!"

I miss laughing with my friends.

I know I'm far from the only unhappy person in the world, but it just feels like that right now. I know it's silly and self-centered, but I am sick and tired of *being there* for Mom. I want someone to *be there* for me. And it's not going to happen and I want to just wallow in self-pity for a while but that's not going to happen, Loretta, so you may as well snap out of it. This is a setback, nothing more. Mom isn't dead or dying. Jeff has his amazing job and you have your freedom and your money and your beautiful little house in the foothills with the pool in the backyard. None of this is permanent. It just feels like it. So many people are so much worse off.

Case in point is Jenny Brown, who lives in my neighborhood. We're not friends because our children's ages don't conform, but we run in similar circles, so I have known *of* Jenny for years. I know that she has had three kids go through the local schools. Jenny has chaired the Orange Grove Middle School Fundraiser Vegas Night for three years in a row and is very active in fundraising for the Tucson Botanical Gardens.

Jenny Brown's life is perfect. On Facebook. Her photos are centered and color-coordinated. She gets those family portraits where everyone dons identical shades of dusty blue and khaki, and position themselves on the slopes of Mount

Lemmon at sunset or over at Saguaro National Park, all smiles, nobody squinting into the light. Her husband is an attorney, who also teaches courses over at the Law School at the U of A. One of their girls is a debate champion at Santa Rita High School. Naturally. And the Brown family vacations! Disneyworld and Aspen and Cape Cod. A couples' getaway to Napa Valley. All photographs lovingly curated online for people to post insincere comments about how awesome things must be.

In reality, however, Jennifer is miserable. I know this because she calls up our common friend, Edie, and sobs to her almost daily. In reality, Jenny Brown and her attorney husband are going through a rather awful divorce. Jenny has no money, her kids all hate her, her job sucks. But there she is on Social Media, waving to the camera with the Golden Gate Bridge in the background, her hair lovingly kissed by a cool San Francisco breeze, her blue eyes untouched by lines. The caption reads chirpily: "Hey there, Frisco! I sure did miss ya!"

I would have no idea about this if Edie hadn't told me. Part of me frankly doesn't believe it. Jenny Brown's smile looks completely unforced. For all I know, those photos were taken years ago. Everything is deceptive. Everything is a false picture of brittle happiness.

Mom's house is cold. I dig around in her dresser till I find a pair of alpaca wool socks with crazy candy cane stripes. I slide around on the tiles in stockinged feet. It's funny how the homes here get so cold. I drink Mom's K-cup coffee while the morning news, and feel helpless. So I get ready to go Agave Springs again. And again.

The days are all just one day on repeat. There is some progress, but not much, and I come back home in the evening and slide around the chilly tiles in the fuzzy socks. There seems little point to it all.

Mom tells me what items she needs and I get them. Today she needs Efferdent for her dentures, which is good; she's thinking about something other than the pain. One of the special, extra-long, padded ice packs I ordered for her on Amazon has arrived. I want time to pass quickly; I am nervous that time is passing too quickly. She is constantly putting an ice-pack on her leg. She's got to be numb.

I feel hope. My mother can roll over better, without yelping out in pain. But then there is another setback, her bowels. Almost two weeks of not eliminating. I hadn't really been paying adequate attention when the nurses warned that such a lengthy delay before surgery while taking opioid pain pills might cause "some disruption." And now it's a week *since* surgery and Mom hasn't had a bowel movement since the day she fell walking Wally in the park! It's a horrifying thought. Now, her system is coming back to life slowly and it hurts. I honestly can't imagine how she must feel. Really, two weeks? Good God. The catch 22 here is this: her constipation hurts, and the narcotics help keep the pain manageable, but they cause more constipation. I am Alice in Wonderland going down the rabbit hole.

Days start crawling by again, but now they are mortifying for both of us. I chirp to Mom that it is no big deal. My stomach clenches. I can hear her weeping as she sits on the toilet. I want to go in and comfort her; I want to run away; I want to scream at the staff. Nobody appears to be doing anything.

We need more pain medication. When we speak to the aides, they say: "I'll tell the nurse." When we speak to the nurse, she says blandly that she is "working on it." I know they have other patients. I see and hear them. I just don't care. Screw the other patients, this is my mother. I confront a nurse in the hallway. She looks at me like I am a stupid child. "I'm working on a colostomy bag," she states. The hall is choking with the smell of shit. I tell my mother that the nurse is busy. I can tell Mom is disappointed with me, but she doesn't say so.

I text Jeff and Sadie. Jeff is kind and asks how he can help. My adversity has turned him into the affectionate husband I've always longed for. He tells me how much he misses and loves me. I am so incredibly grateful for him. Sadie gives me some token minutes of conversation and I lap them up.

Their lives are going on without me. They do not need me. I know this is not entirely true, but it gnaws at me. It would be far worse, of course, if Jeff told me their lives were falling apart in my absence. But at least then someone other than Mom would need me. I try to look ahead. I can't look ahead. I can't see a future in which my mother is fully ambulatory. I know that she will be, but I can't see it. I can't seem to get out of the tunnel vision that focuses solely on Agave Springs and getting through literally one day at a time.

I tell my mother that she will be skipping circles around me in a week or two. But in the back of my mind, I see myself having to sell her home, pack her things. I tell her that she will be settled back at her place, cozy and warm, shortly.

I feel guilty every evening when I depart, thinking she wants me to stay later. But I establish a system: I leave about a half hour after her evening pain pill, when Mom starts relaxing and dozing off. The relief I feel when I leave is palpable, but when I get to her home, I do nothing. I fall asleep. I am not relieved.

I speak to Sadie on the phone. There has been some girl drama. She cries, she swears about her friends. She asks when I am going to be home. She asks if she can buy a pair of Lululemon leggings for $119. She tells me how much she hates Trig class. And her best friend, Caroline. She complains that Jeff makes her walk Rosie. She swears, though tentatively; she sighs deeply. I don't understand anything, Sadie tells me. The delight I feel from her small confidences buoys me for hours.

I can't concentrate on books or tv at Mom's, so I go to bed again at nine. I wake up before five. After I wash up and get dressed, I turn on the television. I search my computer and phone for new political stories, but nothing much has happened overnight except the latest episode of *Saturday Night Live*. I recall Jeff and me, drinking wine and watching the show together, making snide comments about the skits.

My skin is dry. My muscles are tight. My only time outdoors is walking from the parking lot to the rehab entrance, and back out, or walking down a bit from my mother's house to collect her mail at a box at the end of Poinsettia Street. At least we decided to stop the newspapers that had been relentlessly piling up on the kitchen table. I'd thrown a bunch of them in the recycling bin already anyway; she is not going to read them later.

She has a bad night. Terrible pain. No sleep. For all the patients in her wing, there was only one aide on duty overnight. She is writhing in pain, and there has been some kind of disconnect with the overnight nurse, who told Mom *once again* that she could not have her pain pill. My mother is moaning and no one will do anything. She grabs the bars on the side of her bed and arches her back. Her arms look like tendon-y sticks. She cries. And aide stops me in the hallway and tells me they'll have to take my mother to the Emergency Room if she doesn't stop screaming.

The day nurse comes in and gives Mom a pill. It will not kick in for fifteen minutes or so, and I sit next to the bed and listen while she moans softly.

I can't comfort her. I cannot bring her a treat. I cannot hug her. I cannot tell her that it will all be over soon because I have no idea where it will be over. I cannot do anything but sit nearby on the rust-brown loveseat next to the bed and maybe bring over her water, or pass her the lip balm. It has been only five months since my father died. Mom had been his full-time caregiver for years. She was supposed to have the relief of no longer caring for him. She was supposed to have the expelled breath of a longtime illness finally over. She was supposed to have a time just for her.

I talk to Jeff on the phone when I get back to Mom's house at night. When he asks what's wrong, I tell him I'm just tired. I am tired. He tells me how wonderful I'm being for Mom, but I just feel tired

Mom has more bad days, usually from wanting her pill, which never comes on time. It is unclear whether the delay is due to the nurse or to the pharmacy. It doesn't matter. Mom moans with almost every breath, quietly. I wonder if she is aware that she is doing it. Mom asks me to ask the nurse for her pill. The nurse tells me "ten minutes." Ten minutes later, Mom asks me again to find out from the nurse where her pill is. The nurse stares at me behind her glasses and moves slowly.

My mother is crying. She is crying for her pain pill because she cannot move her bowels and the cramps hurt. It annoys me that *this* is her pain, when she has a broken hip. It annoys me that it has been almost three weeks since her fall, and she is still barely moving. It annoys me that I have to sit here hour after hour. Why do I sit? Is someone asking me to do so? Of course not. I am doing it because I cannot *not* do it.

I hate myself. I read. Mom tells me she wants to go to sleep, so I should turn off the lights and go. I drive back to her house. It's cold there. This will never end, this cycle of visits and crying and the terrible smells and the terrible sight of my mother crying in pain and humiliation because she needs to be changed and she can't do it herself. Oh, it is terrible and it will never end.

The world goes on outside of us. Mom's neighbor on the corner has put out bunny and chick decorations nestled in among the cacti outside her house. The days are becoming hot in earnest. It was 88 degrees today, they said on the news. I wasn't outdoors long enough to notice much of anything. I miss Jeff. I miss laughing with Marci and the rest of my girlfriends.

I have bad days; I have better days. I don't cry anymore, although my mother cries more. I try to tell Jeff what's been going on, but I don't want to re-live it in the telling, so I just tell him that things are getting a little better but that we are taking baby steps.

Now that we are getting closer to Easter, the flowers are blooming like crazy at Mom's. There is bougainvillea cascading down the wall on the edge of her patio. Its fuchsia glare seems unreal, manufactured. I take a few photos on my phone to show Mom. She will be happy to see her flowers.

The days get worse. And then suddenly they get better.

I am in awe of the Agave Springs staff, so completely matter-of-fact when they come in to change my mother's bedding. They never complain. How do you get into doing a job like this? But thank God, people do. Once the horror of that pain is gone, Mom has energy to concentrate on her therapy again.

I feel like I can exhale a little bit, but I'm so used to being taut and nervous that it's difficult to unwind. I find I cannot sleep, whereas all the previous evenings, my head hit the pillow at nine. I am proud of Sadie, grateful for Jeff. No one has had even a minor crisis in my absence.

I drive back down to Tucson for a couple days to get some fresh clothes and to pretend I have an existence other than holding vigil at Agave Springs.

I listen to an audiobook on the road. The narrator is an actor from the show *Mad Men*, John Slattery. But I have no idea what the book's title is or what it's about. There are more trucks on the highway than one would expect on a Saturday morning. I can't wait to pull into my little paved driveway on Calle Bendita.

When I get home, I'm not relieved. I feel stupid and powerless. There are so many loose ends. There are so many simultaneous actions going on. I want to hide in the master bedroom and pretend to nap. I am intimidated by the basics. These things were all very simple before, or at least, tolerable and familiar. Making Sadie's lunch for school feels alien and clumsy, like I'm doing it with oven mitts on.

Jeff is beautiful and comfortable. He hugs me, welcoming me home. He pours me glasses of a wonderful, heady Spanish wine. Sadie remains as elusive as ever. Maybe she has become slightly better-humored. Her depths are mysterious, but I need to know more. We go shopping, she and I. We do not buying much of anything, but the time we spend together re-knits us to each other. I buy her the sweet iced coffees and those Japanese iced teas that she loves, filled with tapioca pearls. Her hair is brown again; she has braided it and looks, though I would never use the word in her presence, absolutely fetching.

I drive back up from Tucson again to Mom's house and then head over to Agave Springs. I am vaguely irritated that someone has parked a white SUV in my usual spot, right across from the entryway. Smiling therapists tell me how impressive Mom is, how great her progress has been. *She is very motivated*, they say. *She makes all the other patients look like slackers*, they say.

Mom and I talk about how happy she will be in her own home. Therapists will come to the house once a week for six weeks to help Mom along after she is settled back in her home. We are so relieved that her house is all on one level. It seems every nurse, social worker or therapist asks about stairs. How many stairs are there?

Sadie texts me. She is elated. Jessica and Caroline have invited her to come along with her to see a concert somewhere in Phoenix. I panic for a second, but it's not going to be at State Farm Arena or Footprint Center. It's some non-threatening barely-out-of-her-teens girl singer who made it big on YouTube or something. Sadie's only fourteen. The girls will need a chaperone.

A few weeks ago, the idea of my teenaged daughter being carted up a hundred miles to see a concert in the city, with people vaping weed or whatever they do these days, would have made my head explode. Now it calms me. I think: maybe I can salvage something of a relationship with my daughter out of this; I'll be the Nice Parent, the Cool Mom who lets her (very mature, Honor Roll-earning) daughter attend her first concert.

Jessica's dad will drive them all in his sensible minivan, Sadie writes. God Bless Jessica's Dad, taking all the girls from Tucson to Phoenix and back to Tucson – all in one night. And on *a school night*. Jessica's dad is a flipping saint. I miss Sadie, but when we're together all we do is argue.

It's so incredibly refreshing to think about something outside this room.

I can now worry about mundane things like Easter. I can worry about Sadie's upcoming birthday, and Mother's Day looming in the not so distant future. I can worry about abstractions, like Mom being at home alone. It's much more fun than worrying about her lying in her bed, moaning for a pill. I worry about buying all the food items we will need for a decent Easter supper. I worry that Jeff will not know the precise way to make the double-baked potatoes, if it comes to that. Can I ask Sadie to do them? Will that offend her or thrill her? If I am not around, if I am shepherding my mother or helping her ease back into life in her house, will Jeff and Sadie be able to do the million little unimportant things that become crucial on holidays?

There is a marked change for the better in Mom's existence, here in this small room that never quite loses the smell of pee. Without the electric atmosphere of constant pain, we can talk. Without a dose of powerful narcotics every four hours, we can talk without interruption. Without her moaning and begging for her pill, we can relax. Mom is unleashed; she can't stop talking, it seems. She starts making plans. We must go the bank together when she gets home, Mom tells me. We need to donate more of Dad's old stuff to Goodwill and clear out the guest room.

For me, it's a more difficult transition; my stomach is still constantly in knots. Mom doesn't quite remember what she went through, thank goodness. Now when I arrive in the mornings, she is smiling and dressed and already seated happily in her chair.

The nurses do not have to come in so frequently. We talk and talk. Mom doesn't nap anymore, with her mouth open like a bird. She requests more items from home. A bra, shampoo, stamps and envelopes so she can pay her bills. A candy bar. The other residents of the facility look at her as she walks past their rooms with the help of a walker. Her steps are more than twice their prior length. The therapists applaud her progress.

Mom is now able to be angry with herself that the fall even happened. She is eager to get home. It has been four weeks since the fall. We don't talk about the dog, though. I start, once, to bring up Wally, and her eyes fill with tears. I tell her that he's happy.

Four weeks lost, she says. How can I just lose four weeks?

I wonder too.

Now that we know that she will be going home in a few days, I throw out garbage and put away laundry. I do the dishes. Mom will be coming home on Good Friday. We joke about how it's a *really* Good Friday this year. I will stay with Mom to make sure she can do alright her first days back, and then Jeff and Sadie will drive up from Tucson.

I'm so happy to get Mom out of Agave Springs that I fill out the Exit Questionnaire with uniformly positive, practically glowing, reviews. I just want it past me. I thank Pearlie and Stephanie and all the rest of the staff that I cursed internally for three weeks straight.

I wheel Mom down the piss-stained carpet and around the vacantly staring, long-term patients who line the hallways in their wheelchairs. When we get into the car and pull out into the sunshine, Mom squeals a little bit and fumbles around in the glove compartment for some extra sunglasses.

She tells me she would have died if I hadn't been around. It's not at all true, but I am glad I was able to help. I would never have been able to do all of this without Jeff really stepping up at home. I'm so lucky his job is allowing this extra flexibility these days. Mom settles down into her sofa with an icepack on her hip, and we just sit quietly.

On Easter, Jeff and Sadie arrive with a huge bouquet of balloons and a *Welcome Home* banner that we hang over the fireplace. Sadie has prepared not only the twice-baked potatoes, but also the asparagus and some wild mushroom risotto. Jeff heats up the ham. We have far too much food and wine. We make far too many toasts. Mom shows off with her walker, pacing through the living room like a spry young thing, not a woman who was crying in her bed just days ago. Years have left her face.

After dinner, we decide to go out to the patio, among the bougainvillea, and drink some more. Mom will only sip a little, she says, since she read online that it may impede her healing progress. She is adamant to never be frail and dependent again. She stands up a little too fast and sways a little.

Jeff, who had been absently looking at something on his phone, places it hastily on the counter as he grasps Mom's elbow.

"Let's save the jumping for tomorrow, ok?" he laughs. Mom laughs too.

He helps her out to the rattan seats, her arm in his. I remain in the kitchen, pouring orange juice and prosecco into Waterford tumblers. We made it, I marvel. What an absolutely unexpected challenge, but now it's effectively over and we can be cautiously optimistic from here on out. Life is infinitely strange.

Jeff's phone buzzes unexpectedly and I jump, spilling the orange juice. Some of it gets onto the back of the phone, so I pick it up to wipe down the case. He's gotten a message from Marci. I can't wait to hook up with her this week in our usual spot at the park. She's been so helpful, always in touch with Jeff and take care of things in my absence during all the craziness so I wouldn't have to worry.

I can't wait to catch up with Marci and see what her Easter was like with Jim and the kids. Jim's parents are at an assisted living facility in Tucson, and I'll bet they're all on her way back home from there right now, ready to settle down and prepare for the week ahead. And there'll be dog-walking and laughter and children who grow up and surprise you with their adult-ness at the strangest times.

Can't wait till I see you again.

I hold Jeff's phone in my hands till the message notification disappears. I wipe my hands on Mom's bunny-covered Easter dish towels. I had to really dig to find those holiday towels in her linen closet. I made sure they were out before we got returned here, triumphant, on Good Friday. Mom actually used to have all her fancy holiday tea towels organized chronologically. The Easter Bunnies normally were in a neat pile right next to the shamrock and Valentine towels. But when I searched the other night, I found them folded in among the pillow cases.

Dad's death took a lot out of her; sixty years is a long time to be with someone. It's not at all surprising that Mom got a little slack about her putting away all her holiday décor. Especially after what she's been through, that we've both been through now.

I remember now the way everything sparkled on New Year's Eve, how Tucson looked like a handful of jewels scattered down the foothills. And it seems like I am falling down that mountainside myself, leaving traces of sparkling brightness in my wake as I tumble down and and down.

OPENING NIGHT
AT THE RIO SALADO LITTLE
THEATRE

The dog in the apartment downstairs kept me up all night. Little bugger may be small, but he barks and whines and howls. They're in the middle of potty-training him, so they're up at all hours, making sure he pees out back and not on the carpet. Normally, it wouldn't phase me; dogs are the best, especially puppies. But at this point, I don't care if he craps on their heads; I need sleep. It's Tech Week and I'm irritable as Hell.

It will be a miracle if we pull this one off. A real, honest to God miracle. We've had close shaves before, but Dave was always around to wave his magic wand and fix things then. But Dave took a powder for this one. Our first show in almost two years, the first post-Covid production for Rio Salado, and our fearless leader is gone. Our triumphant comeback is in grave danger of becoming our last hurrah.

Thanks, Dave. Thanks bunches, dude. This was supposed to be *his* show. I was supposed to blend into the background as always, Franklin the Assistant Director. The one who writes down everyone's blocking. The one who reads lines for missing actors and who stays on-book to see if the cast is getting their lines and movement down right.

If we don't have a particular prop, for instance, I would simply tell Dave and voila: it's his problem. He coordinates with Nina and gets it done. Nina, however, doesn't much like me, so we've only just now gotten some of our important props, like the wine glasses. The AD takes the calls from people telling me they're not going to make it to rehearsal and relay that information to Dave, who then figures out which scenes we should run that night. I never had to figure those things out because I was not the Director.

Except now I am.

Dave's elderly father ("the Aged Parent," Dave calls him, but naturally I am the only one who gets the subtle reference to *David Copperfield*) in Bonita Springs, Florida, has suffered a stroke, and Dave flew out there three weeks ago. So I am supposed to shepherd this rag-tag bunch into putting together a show.

"The cast is in great shape, Frankie," Dave told me before he left. "Most of them are off-book, and everyone has their blocking down. You'll have to coordinate a bit with Carlos and Stefan for Lighting and Sound cues, but you know this is a simple enough show from a technical standpoint. You're a pro. You could practically run this production in your sleep. It should all go pretty smoothly, and I'll be back as soon as Dad's out of medical danger."

I was so flattered by Dave's confidence in my ability to direct this production that I didn't do much more than squeak out "Thanks," and shake his hand before he left. Dave is so convincing that he even had *me* believing in me for a second.

Until I started actually trying to run rehearsals, that is. Then everything became, if you'll excuse the expression, a cluster-fuck. The cast sensed my incapacity to rally them, and instead of being helpful, they walked all over me. Actors started coming into rehearsal late, without calling or even sending a text. Jill suddenly can't remember her lines – and keeps yelling out "Line!" --which is what you're supposed to do when you're stuck. Usually. When there is a Director on hand.

In the normal way of doing things, the *Assistant Director*, who is watching the script, helps out the actors by staying on-book. That used to be my job. But obviously now there's no one free to prompt Jill, so we all have to wait till creaky old Rachel stops what she's working on and feeds her a line. Good old Rachel.

Another of our actors, Greg, takes it upon himself to start *directing* other actors. "You're doing it wrong," he states to Peter, who normally doesn't like taking even helpful, supportive tips, let alone unsolicited commentary from another cast member. Pete ignores Greg (we here at the Rio Salado Little Theatre spend much of our rehearsals ignoring Greg; it's a favorite pass-time), who then repeats himself.

"You're doing it wrong. You're supposed to put the wine glass on the coffee table after your line. I have it written down it down in my script."

"Why don't you worry about your own character?" Peter returns.

"I'm trying to, but when you do things wrong, it throws me off." retorts Greg.

This would be the perfect opportunity to be a Leader, to Direct. But I am a fairly non-confrontational person and I'm not really sure what the best way to go here is. Also, part of me would dearly love to see a shouting match -- or better yet, a fist fight -- between these two buffoons. Luckily, I don't have to make any sort of decision because Mallory comes to the rescue.

"You're both acting like assholes. Shut up so we can get this goddamned scene finished. I need a cigarette." She growls.

Good old Mallory.

The Rio Salado Little Theatre was founded in 1978. Our first "home" was a tiny storefront just off Rio Salado Parkway in South Phoenix. The original members wanted a place to perform experimental theater and various forms of performance art. They did a lot of wacky shit back then, I guess. I've heard stories from some of the old-timers that psychedelic drugs may or may not have been involved in some productions.

At any rate, after a few years of performing to near empty houses for a few local hippies, Rio Salado changed its fare to more mainstream programming to keep itself afloat. A few industrious members invested in decent seats and a curtain, and eventually the Little Theatre did productions of Albee and Wilder and Miller that brought in some people. But the storefront off Rio Salado was grungy and terrible, and didn't attract the older lady crowd (aka the life-blood of amateur theatre). Times were iffy.

Then came the big break: Rio Salado "inherited" the space abandoned by Desert

Footlights Community Theatre. On Central! Having a dedicated performance space in a decent neighborhood is an absolute godsend to a struggling theatre group. It means you no longer have to rely on the benevolence of a church that lets you use its basement when the local AA groups aren't, or the red-tape bureaucracy of a park district allowing you to rent its tiny stage – as long as *their* precious programming, like youth karate classes, doesn't preempt you. It meant no more tip-toeing over broken bottles and God knows what other nasty debris, clutching your car keys and glancing furtively around you as you depart the storefront after rehearsal.

Suddenly Rio Salado had a *real* stage and *real* wings and a backstage area that fit more than three people, and *actual* seats instead of folding chairs. The group gained a respectability that they hadn't truly earned. And all because Desert Footlights was bankrupted by one Marybeth Norton, an embezzling Treasurer who literally skipped town with their profits, small though they were.

Rio Salado Little Theatre had its heyday in the Nineties, putting on decent productions to full houses, and gaining enough new, due-paying members that we could pay our rent and even help us buy light and sound boards. We even gained little bit of a reputation in our part of the Valley. The *Arizona Republic* did a story on us in 1996, that was featured in the "Weekend's Best" section. *Phoenix-Area Theater Group Brings in Laughs, Crowds*, read the headline. A copy of that article hangs in our lobby in a nice frame.

Rio Salado's had an up and down time since then, but Dave's appearance on the scene in the early 2000s certainly helped keep the group alive. The fact that Dave is preternaturally youthful and charismatic surely has to explain why we have an excess of female volunteers. I mean, community theatre is always going to be female-heavy. It's just the nature of the beast. But would we have *quite* so many eager-to-work ladies if we didn't have David as our charming figurehead? Would there be quite so many ladies who distribute our programs, work as ushers, and sift through decades of old crap, organizing it into neat bins marked "flapper costumes," "feathered hats" and "seventies-era men's neckties"?

Thanks to Dave's efforts, Rio Salado got some big-hitter angel donors, whose generosity has gone a long way to keep this scruffy place going. Dave had just started in as Artistic Director when I joined about fifteen years ago. I was new to Phoenix and missed the community theater scene we had back in Minneapolis.

The funny thing is, I don't much like acting; I'm a behind-the-scenes guy. I used to Stage Manage quite a bit, though that can get a little stressful. It's fun work, calling cues to Light and Sound, getting actors ready to go. As I've gotten older, though, I prefer the more leisurely role of Assistant Director. As an AD, your "work" is effectively done once the actors are off-book. You can slide into Tech Week and production relatively unscathed. Not so when you are pushed, naked and shivering, into the role of Director. We are so screwed.

*

I need to clear my head, so I tell Maxine that I'll be back in ten minutes. I walk out of the dim, air-conditioned interior of Rio Salado to the white sunlight of a Phoenix afternoon. Even at the time of year, that sun hits you like an offensive lineman. Naturally, I left my sunglasses inside, but I don't want to go back and grab them because then I'd have to explain my fleeing the scene of the crime to Maxine, who is hanging around making preparations for tonight, stocking the bathrooms with paper towels and toilet paper, so I bow my head and squint at the sidewalk. Six hours till we open.

The programs have all been printed, the tickets are ready to go, thanks to Priya. And the little hippy girl who is our Wardrobe Mistress has cleaned and ironed all the costumes. Stefan's light cues went great last night, though honestly, *Rumors* is basically a "lights on/lights off" kind of production. Thank goodness. A Neil Simon farce is not the type of show that requires specials and follow spots. We have only one important sound cue, a snippet of the old Richie Valens tune, *La Bamba*, that's played briefly near the end of Act Two. So Carlos will be fine.

All-purpose helper Doreen has vacuumed the house; pre-show ticket sales have been steady. We'll have an audience tonight, if not a decent performance. People want to get back into the theater, especially here in good old Arizona where many people spent the last two years pretending Covid didn't actually exist.

Last night was, putting it mildly, a shit show. It was our final dress rehearsal and Dustin *didn't show up*. Literally didn't come to the final dress rehearsal before we open tonight. *Rumors* is an ensemble piece; actors need an intimate communication and trust with each other. Dustin plays Glenn, a key role. It's crucial that the actors are comfortable bouncing their lines quickly and effortlessly off each other. Crucial. This is what I meant when I said that this cast doesn't think of me as a real Director, as their actual leader. No one would ever do this to Dave.

I called and texted Dustin, about seventy-five times, delaying our final run-through for more than an hour. Finally Danny Rosen admitted that Dustin posted on Facebook that he was going to a cattle call audition downtown for the chance at a role as an extra in *The Mandalorian*. I'm not making this up. The damned *Madalorian*. Unbelievable.

After some shuffling around, I got Maxine, our stage manager, on script to read out Glenn's lines. Now, Maxine de Guzman is a wonderful volunteer for Rio Salado, and we all owe her a huge debt of gratitude for her years of tirelessly painting flats, pulling props, and sewing costumes, but there are preschoolers who can read lines faster than she does. Everyone's timing was off as a result. And since we didn't have "Glenn" physically on the stage, their blocking was thrown off as well. And honestly, their blocking lacked finesse before this happened.

Timing off, blocking ignored, actors missing. What else can go wrong? Please, Universe, do not answer this question.

God, I wish this was autumn. We could've done a drama. Comedy is too hard. Too many intangibles need to work in order for a comedy to succeed. It's relatively simple to get an audience to cry. We could've done 'Night, Mother or Our Town and we'd have an infinitely easier time than with this one. But it's February, and in February Rio Salado does comedies. The Little Theater That

Could is consistent in our productions, if not in our production quality.

Even if we are stuck with doing comedy, I wish to God we'd have picked one with fewer actors. I know the rationale: the more actors we cast, the more friends and family will purchase tickets. It's a smart move, financially. And that's why you always see so many amateur theatres putting on productions of *You Can't Take It With You* -- an enormous cast size to bring in the audiences.

This is the same mentality that keeps other amateur theater companies performing *Annie* every other year. Casting a show with kids is like printing money. The downside is that then you have to do a show with kids. Which takes a special form of super-human. I don't think even Dave could sustain it.

But truly, they could've gone with a three-actor play like *Art* or even done *Barefoot in the Park* and had fewer actors to deal with. But they said that *Art* was "too pretentious" and that Rio Salado has done *Barefoot* more than three times in our history, so *Rumors* it was.

I should be happy they didn't go balls out and put on *Noises Off.* Can you even imagine? A two-level set that needs to be rotated between acts, plus British accents. Oh, boy. Not that Omar and Stu haven't been itching to build more sets, but we're just getting our sea legs back here after being on forced sabbatical for over eighteen months. But I break out in hives just *thinking about* tackling a production like *Noises Off* here without Dave.

Rumors is an uncharacteristically sensible choice, given our play-reading committee. Solid, single-set Neil Simon ensemble piece that hasn't been performed to death yet by local community theatres. Usually, our committee decides that Rio Salado should put on some incredibly difficult to stage behemoth like *Les Miserables*. When Dave gently explains that Rio Salado has a budget of about $5,000 per production, and that the set-construction alone would be bankrupt us, they usually rein it in a little.

Except of course for the irrepressible Paula Gertz, Rio Salado's resident cheerleader. Paula has an endless list of shows she wants to have Rio Salado produce because she wants to star in all of them. The woman's knowledge of theater is exhaustive.

"How about *Evita*?" she asks.

"We don't have the orchestra, Paula." Dave responds mildly.

"How about *42nd Street*?"

"We will never get enough female tap dancers, Paula, let alone any male ones."

She never stops: "How about *Sweeney Todd*?"

"We do not have nearly enough strong male vocalists, Paula. That show requires at least six. We have only Gene who can sing, and he's a tenor. Who's going to play Todd?"

Paula doesn't give up either; she actually thinks she could play Mrs. Lovett, despite the fact that her range is too narrow, her ability to do accents is atrocious, and she can't act her way out of a paper bag. But to give Paula credit: she is loyal to Rio Salado Little Theatre. Paula's been out there painting flats, cleaning out our storage space, writing up blurbs to post on our Facebook page, and being a general good sport for almost ten years. But with her voice, she is never leaving the ranks of the ensemble.

A few years ago, Paula auditioned for the role of Laura Wingfield, the frail young waif in *The Glass Menagerie*. Paula did so, despite being closer in age to the character of Amanda Wingfield, Laura's mother. Of course, Paula didn't get the role, which I think went to Meredith Taylor, that tiny little powerhouse who used to do professional theater before she settled down and started having babies. Rio Salado sure got lucky with that one. What's funny is that Amanda Wingfield is by far a meatier role, which any actor will tell you. It's one of those dream roles all women want to play at some point in their lives. But Paula couldn't audition for Amanda without tacitly acknowledging that she was no longer equipped to play the ingénue.

Paula has similar trouble accepting the truth about the amount of talent she possesses as well. Dave can sweet-talk her into the best bit-parts (servants, maids, the best friend who makes a token appearance), which usually satisfies her. For *Rumors*, Dave cast her as Officer Pudney, the female cop, who has maybe three lines. It is the perfect role for her. There are no small actors, Paula. Just some not very good ones.

Ok, I'm being unfair to Paula, who really is a good sport and does a ton of work around here. It's been somewhat awkward between us ever since that disastrous relationship we attempted to kindle back in 2016. At least, we're still cordial. At least, no one tried to force the other to leave Rio Salado and go work at Stage Light Theatricals in Chandler or some other competitor venue. I don't mind that she and Carlos are an item now.

Community Theatre is notorious for making and breaking romances. There is a strange camaraderie when you work closely and intensely with the same group for a three month period, and then go back to being mere acquaintances. I've seen theatre relationships break up several marriages, and not just here at Rio Salado. Theatre creates strange bedfellows. Or maybe strange bedfellows like to create theatre? Dave always jokes about the position of men in this microcosm.

"Only in community theatre can mediocre guys like me be the center of attention and play a romantic lead. This doesn't happen in the real world." he says.

Dave is *far* from mediocre and he knows it. The guy is seriously movie star good-looking; all the women at Rio Salado talk about him, even the ones old enough to be his mother. But he's right about the position of men. They are always in demand. And not just because many of us like to wave around our power tools and pretend we know what we're doing when we're constructing a set. There's just a constant need for male players.

Rio Salado has about six or maybe seven men who audition for us regularly. All with varying degrees of talent. It's an effort every season to find different female-centric plays we haven't already done too many times. There are only so many productions of *Steel Magnolias* and *Crimes of the Heart* one can stomach, after all. Women come in to audition for us, and there might be six equally talented gals we could cast in any given female role. But unless we're putting on *Death of a Salesman* or something, where about ten guys all want to play Willy Loman, we are constantly shaking all the local trees to find enough guys. The general sentiment is that if you have a heartbeat and a penis, you'll get cast in community theatre.

We've been so strapped for men that we've done Shakespeare productions where half the male characters are played by women. We just change the names a little. We've had a Benvolia, Mercutia, Mother Laura (instead of Friar Laurence) and the Princess of Verona (instead of the Prince) for *Romeo and Juliet*. We had to keep Romeo male, of course. Though our Romeo was – well, let's just say he was no Romeo. Our Juliet couldn't stand him. After stabbing herself in grief over Romeo's death for three weekends in a row, Juliet famously proclaimed to Dave on closing night, "I can't believe I made it through the run, playing against that clown. I am the greatest fuckin' actress in the world" and lit up an enormous blunt.

Rio Salado's lack of (adequately talented) men has been a problem for ages. A few years back, we put on *Picnic*. A classic, but it requires its leading man to be both young and sexy, enough to entice the village cutie to leave her home at the end. We couldn't get anyone to audition; all the men who showed up were over fifty, too fat, or both.

Dave, being Dave, somehow found a kid to play the part. The guy *looked* perfect: chiseled, early twenties, Hollywood-level good looks. Except he couldn't speak. The kid was a complete mush-mouth, swallowed all his lines. If you were more than ten feet away, you had no idea what he was saying. Luckily, his character didn't have too many lines, so he spent most of his time onstage standing there, looking smoldering. The kid had *that* part down.

Our production of *Picnic* was a rousing success, in spite of Mush-mouth's performance. That was all thanks to Dave's stellar direction; he can get the stiffest rookie to sound good onstage. He's a flipping magician. No, it's not that: Dave is just such a nice person that all his actors want to do better just to please him. It's a joy to watch. Which makes my current plight even sadder. I know that the cracks in this show's armor could have been better patched by Dave's light-hearted touch, not my ham-fisted reprimands. I get it. *I* wouldn't even want to put my best effort forth for me; why should they?

Even in the odd occurrence of a Dave mess-up, somehow the guy can still turn the situation from mortifying into comic legend. For example, no matter how much Paula pleads for them, Rio Salado no longer puts on musicals, not since we started having to actually pay Music Directors. Believe me, you *have to* pay your Music Directors. Otherwise, you'll end up with someone like Charlene Daymont as an MD. Charlene can't even play piano. We had her music direct a production of *Promises, Promises* back maybe ten years ago. She sweet-talked Dave into it. It was a rare miss for King David, I'll admit.

Anyway, Charlene insisted on rehearsing everyone with cd backing tracks. Which is fine, except the actors got used to singing along with them and not with live accompaniment. And when the band came in during Tech Week, they played all the songs in a different key and tempo than the cast had gotten used to. The actors were fumbling entrances and messing up every song. And these were Burt Bacharach songs with some funky rhythms. It was hellish. But we pulled it off because the old people who subscribe to the Rio Salado Little Theatre are generally forgiving, and largely hard of hearing.

That lame production of *Promises* gained hilarious mythic status here. Dave, instead of attempting to sweep that production under the carpet and relegate it into the dustbin of memory, made the show sort of a hilarious metaphor for a fuck-up. He'll say: "There's good news, there's bad news, and then there's *Promises, Promises* News." If someone makes a gaffe in rehearsal, Dave will coyly say, "Is that Burt Bacharach music I hear?" Instantly, the tension is diffused; instead of dwelling on the mistakes we're making currently, we can look back and laugh at the fiasco of *Promises, Promises*. It's fantastic.

Dave can do that. I cannot. I couldn't even stop Priya from pre-emptively ruining our production of *Rumors* with her preshow music.

Priya teaches Language Arts at Desert Marigold Middle School. One of her students, she told me, is a gifted clarinet player. Wouldn't it be a lovely idea, Priya mused, if this student were to play her clarinet before the opening curtain? Instead of the recorded pre-show music we usually play. The light-hearted clarinet music will really get the audience in the right frame of mind the show, she said. Let me add that Priya and I had this conversation immediately after she *volunteered to edit our programs.* Program editing is a painstaking, boring, long job that we usually have to beg someone to undertake. I could see where Priya was heading with this one: let the kid play, or your programs will suffer the consequences. Naturally, I replied that we would be delighted to hear the kid play!

It had to be a cracked reed. I understand woodwinds enough to know that a reed that make or break a clarinet performance.

It wasn't her reed.

The actors thought it was a practical joke. Pete Fugel told me they all thought that Ashton Kutcher would burst out from behind the curtain Backstage Left and we'd all have a good laugh about it. I've honestly never heard such horrible playing in my life; not even during a performance of *Music Man,* when Harold Hill's band is *supposed to* sound like crap, but the parents love it anyway. And now it's too late. I can't fire the kid because I never *hired* the kid. Besides that, how do you fire a middle schooler who's been asked by her teacher to perform at a grown-up theatre production without coming across like an ogre?

Long story short: Chiara, I think that's her name, is listed on our freshly-printed programs stacked neatly against the lobby walls. She will play tonight before an almost full house, and it will be so horrific that the audience will asking themselves whether they made a wrong turn somewhere after they passed the box office, and that they ended up in Konrad's Komedy Klub down the road. Because no one could seriously play so badly and yet not realize it, except Priya.

*

This doomed production of *Rumors* will go down in the annals of Rio Salado Little Theatre lore. How our so-called comeback show became our swan song. And as Director, I am the bottom line. The buck stops with me.

Back inside the dark of Rio Salado, I tell Maxine I'm going home for a few hours. I'll see her back here around six, when the cast will start showing up. I need to try to nap. Last night's fiasco with Dustin not showing kept me up until there were birds singing outside my window. When I pull into my apartment complex, I see my downstairs neighbor and her dog coming in from a walk. She waves cheerfully at me, but I pretend not to notice her. I can't deal with life right now.

I shuffle to the mailroom; maybe my *Route Magazine* has arrived. I'm a big fan of Route 66 nostalgia. When we lived in the Twin Cities, Meg and I used to drive from Chicago to Los Angeles, stopping at all the weird and wonderful roadside attractions like the Blue Whale in Catoosa, Oklahoma and Cadillac Ranch in Amarillo, Texas. We took our time, spending weeks driving the Mother Road. It was our tradition every other year. After Meg got sick, we stopped doing the Route. And then later I ended up moving down here to the land of eternal sunshine. I miss those trips.

No magazine. Just my luck these days. I go back to the apartment and turn on the computer. I read every message from the crew – the crew is vital -- but I skim over all the emails from the cast. I'm too tired at this point. Dustin is clearly trying to apologize for ghosting us last night; there are at least four messages from him alone. There are the usual, sweet-but-annoying set of "Break a Leg, you guys!" messages from the cast and crew. It's great for team-building, but clogs the inbox. And then there's a surprise; an email from Dave. He writes:

Hey, Frankie,

Well, you made it through Tech Week. I know how rough Tech can be when it's your first time directing. Nothing seems to go right. But know this: we do this because it's fun. Let me say that again so you remember it: <u>this is fun</u>. Theater lifts us up and takes us out of ourselves when we need a break from what can sometimes be a miserable reality. Knowing that you were able to take the helm when I can't be around has lifted me out of a pretty sad situation here in Florida. I've never worried about the production; I know it will be great. It is already great – because you and all the Rio Salado Family have made this together. Opening Night. There is nothing else on earth like it. Most people will never understand what it feels like to put a show together. But you do, and this night is <u>yours</u>. You have earned all the laughs and all the applause you'll get during this run. Enjoy the ride.

Best, Dave

God-damned Dave. From a thousand-plus miles away, he's still the King.

I decide to join in on the cast email chain, cordially wishing broken limbs to everyone and reminding them that call time tonight is 6:00 pm. I shower, shave, and put on a nice jacket and dress shirt. I even pat on a little cologne.

It's show-time.

I get to the theater, and Greg MacDonald is here already, reciting his lines. Greg is playing Lenny. Which was a huge gamble in casting. Lenny has a doozy of a long monologue at the end of the show, which has to be spoken quickly to come across right, and Greg can have trouble with lines sometimes. Well, if he gets into a jam, Greg can always improvise. Lord knows he's done it before here.

We did a Thriller some years back where Greg played a gruff, but good-hearted cop. At the climax of the show, the Bad Guy revealed his identity and Greg's cop character was supposed to shoot him. It's a great, tight scene that should move like lightning. Except our Sound Guy missed his cue. I forget; it may have been a computer glitch because normally Carlos is super-reliable. At any rate, Greg drew out his prop gun out with a flourish, aimed it at the Bad Guy, and pulled the trigger. There was no sound. Greg froze. The Bad Guy, who was supposed to get shot, also just stood there, sweating under the stage-lights. You could practically taste the panic. And then Greg bellowed "Bang!" and gestured with the prop gun. The Bad Guy fell to the ground, and the audience went just about crazy with applause. Greg's improvisation was perhaps not the smoothest move in the book, but it did the job. And the audience loved it.

"Hey, Greg, Lenny's gonna be on fire tonight," I tell him. Greg stops his pacing and thanks me.

The actors filter in and start getting into make-up. The Box Office crew is already here. God knows our technical crew has been here, fixing last minute glitches, all day. The house has been cleared of all the garbage we've strewn there all week. I smell popcorn. Rio Salado traditionally hands out free paper bags of popcorn for all our performances.

It's a bitch to clean up, but our audience loves it. And they're a loyal bunch, so why not keep them happy?

Peter and Jill run their lines from the opening scene of the play. It's just the two of them together onstage for the first eight minutes or so, and their characters are meant to be highly agitated. After a little slipping, they get the dialogue flowing smoothly, and they high five each other. Paula is running around distributing some insanely large cookies shaped like colorful stars and flowers. "Happy Opening Night!" she sings. I say the same back to her and she hands me a star that says *Congratulations* in frosting. I try it. Delicious.

"Break a leg," I tell her. "Officer Pudney is going to rock! Just make sure you cheat out to say your lines." She nods at me and gives me a thumbs-up.

Jennifer striding around the house like a nut, complaining that the zipper on her evening gown is stuck, and the poor Wardrobe Mistress is following her around, trying to get Jen to stop so she can try to fix it. It's funny: what makes *Rumors* relatively easy to stage also makes it difficult. The show doesn't have *any* costume changes, which is great, and practically never happens in two-act plays. The downside is that every actor needs to be dressed up to go to a gala in New York City. So the men all need to be in tuxedos and the women in evening gowns. Oh, and there's the two cops, but they don't come in till the end. The young woman purses her lips and tugs at Jennifer's zipper, which finally moves. Jen cheers and stalks away, "needing her space" before we open. Wardrobe Gal laughs with relief. She's cute as a button and looks maybe sixteen, but sports a tattoo and a pierced nose, which is really off-putting. I must be getting old.

"I don't think we've had a show with better looking costumes," I tell her. "Super spiffy."

The set really does look great, and the little imperfections are not visible from the House. Omar and Stu did a fine job creating a swanky New York residence here in the middle of our dusty theater. Nina's Prop Table is immaculate. She's kind of a control freak about that, so no surprise. You really want your Properties person (and of course, your Set Decorator) to be detail-oriented. The look and feel of a production rely on them.

We open the House and the actors are all herded backstage. The seats begin to fill and Rio Salado starts echoing with that indistinct murmur of many voices talking to each other. Rachel and Candi seat the patrons. We have several folks who need the wheelchair accessible seats in front. Jill has placed programs on about six seats in the front row, reserving them for her family. This is strictly against Rio Salado policy, but Jill told me that her folks had come in from Prescott to see her tonight, so of course I'm letting it pass.

Chiara gets onstage. Oh, fuck.

She plays alright. She really does. Some squeaks, but nothing near the (*Promises, Promises*) level of badness that we heard in rehearsal. Chiara's entire extended family is here (they've bought tickets for every performance!) and they cheer her so vigorously that the rest of the audience catches on and joins in. And it's decent applause throughout the House. Priya gives her a bear hug backstage. Maxine starts up our recorded message:

"Good Evening and Welcome to the grand re-opening of the Rio Salado Little Theatre. We are so excited to have you back in your seats here where you belong. Please remember to silence all your phones and unwrap all those crinkly candy wrappers before we begin! We remind you that Federal Law prohibits the recording of this production in any way. And absolutely no flash photography! We now invite you to sit back, relax, and enjoy Rio Salado's production of Neil Simon's hilarious comedy, *Rumors*."

The recording is Dave's voice, of course. He recorded it just before he went to Florida. He sounds like a mix of Don Draper and Cary Grant. The audience applauds. There are even a few cries of: "woo-hoo!" And then it's Blackout, Curtain open, Lights up.

*

My actors are -- well, my gosh, they are downright amazing. They play to the house; they play *off* the house. Jill is crazily neurotic as Chris Gorman, absolutely flawless in her first scene. The bickering Ganz's show up, and Greg and Mallory barely come up for air they're timing the dialogue so nicely. The layers keep building. This crowd is fantastic; they're laughing, they're clapping after some laugh lines (I'll have to remind Greg to hold longer for laughs tomorrow night because we wouldn't want to drown out the next line). By the time Danny and Jennifer get onstage as Ernie and Cookie Cusak and start with their corny shtick, the audience is practically rolling in their seats.

After Intermission, we have to delay the start of Act Two because of people buying drinks and chatting happily in the foyer. And then we're back onstage and the momentum is *still* flowing. Finally, the two cops arrive; Paula's Officer Pudney will never be mistaken for a scene-stealer, but it's a solid, solid job by Paula. Greg's extended monologue is just about perfect; the little glitches he encounters *seem to be* intentional because Lenny is distraught. No one notices. And would you believe a standing ovation, enthusiastically led by all six members of Jill's family in the front row reserved seats?

I did this. I helped put this messy, sweet thing together. What a ride.

Rio Salado tradition dictates that the cast and crew meets up at Seamus McCaffery's Pub on Opening Night. We re-live highlights of evening's performance; we praise that awesome crowd; we toast each other. My cast (they *are* my cast, and not Dave's, after all) is jubilant, as well they should be. We Facetime Dave in Florida. It's still light out there. He's on the patio, looking even more handsome than usual with a tan.

"Now don't forget, everyone," Dave warns on Maxine's smartphone. "Don't screw it up tomorrow night!" And everybody laughs.

It's a great time.

Danny confesses that he thinks he may have split his tuxedo pants while dancing to *La Bamba* in the final scene.

"Only you could manage to ruin costume doing a dance scene that's about a minute long," teases Jill.

"Actually the sound cue is only fifteen seconds." Carlos replies, and he certainly would know.

We all laugh.

"Well, make sure you bring that up to our Peerless Wardrobe Woman. Hey, where did she go?" asks Mallory

"Oh, Molly couldn't come out with us tonight," says Paula. "She had a thing to go to. A concert or something, she said."

"I sent her a text about the tux; she said it'll be ok." Danny says.

It's one o'clock in the morning by the time we all slouch out of McCaffery's. Luckily, I was too dazzled by tonight's performance to drink much because it's a bit of a ride back to my place. I'm still feeling giddy that we actually pulled it off. The gas in my Escape is low, so I pull into a Circle K to fill up. Better to err on the side of caution. I've been pretty lucky tonight; don't jinx it now.

There's something pink on the ground next to the gas pump: it's a little plush bunny. I bend down and slip it into my pocket. I'll bring it back home and give it to my downstairs neighbors for their new puppy. It's just the right size for a puppy to chew on. Even though the new pup doesn't know when to shut up, I'm glad they got him. I missed having a dog nearby. I loved old Bixby, their previous dog; now he was a charmer. A Cavalier King Charles Spaniel, cute as a button.

Raina told me she never thought they'd ever be able to love another dog after Bixby died. But I guess she heard from a friend that some swanky shelter in Scottsdale had a purebred Basset Hound puppy. Raina's husband is a sucker for those sad-eyed dogs. She applied at the shelter for the little guy and got him, just like that. Raina feels she was *meant to* have this pup. She's into in all that crazy psychic stuff, so who knows? She may be right.

Tonight I'm going to sleep better than I have all month.

Made in the USA
Monee, IL
18 August 2022

11951366R00108